Waves and Messages

Waves and Messages

JOHN R. PIERCE

This book is the third volume of a revised
and greatly enlarged edition of
Electrons, Waves and Messages,
which was published
in 1956 by Doubleday & Company, Inc.

Published by Anchor Books
Doubleday & Company, Inc.
Garden City, New York

To

W. O. BAKER

who understands science,
technology, and people

The Science Study Series

The Science Study Series offers to students and to the general public the writing of distinguished authors on the most stirring and fundamental topics of science, from the smallest known particles to the whole universe. Some of the books tell of the role of science in the world of man, his technology and civilization. Others are biographical in nature, telling the fascinating stories of the great discoverers and their discoveries. All the authors have been selected both for expertness in the fields they discuss and for ability to communicate their special knowledge and their own views in an interesting way. The primary purpose of these books is to provide a survey within the grasp of the young student or the layman. Many of the books, it is hoped, will encourage the reader to make his own investigations of natural phenomena.

The Series, which now offers topics in all the sciences and their applications, had its beginning in a project to revise the secondary schools' physics curriculum. At the Massachusetts Institute of Technology during 1956 a group of physicists, high school teachers, journalists, apparatus designers, film producers, and other specialists organized the Physical Science Study Committee, now operating as a part of Educational Services Incorporated, Watertown, Massachusetts. They pooled their knowledge and experience toward the design and creation of aids to the learning of physics. Initially their effort was supported by the National Science Foundation, which has continued to aid the program. The Ford Foundation, the Fund for the Advancement of Education, and the Alfred P. Sloan Foundation have also given support. The Committee has created a textbook, an extensive film series, a laboratory guide, especially designed apparatus, and a teachers' source book.

The Series is guided by a Board of Editors consisting of Bruce F. Kingsbury, Managing Editor; John H. Durston, General Editor; Paul R. Brandwein, the Conservation Foundation and Harcourt, Brace & World, Inc.; Samuel A. Goudsmit, Brookhaven National Laboratory; Philippe LeCorbeiller, Harvard University; and Gerard Piel, *Scientific American*.

Biographical Foreword

Publication of *Waves and Messages* completes John R. Pierce's thorough revision, for the Science Study Series, of his widely admired *Electrons, Waves and Messages* (Doubleday, 1956). The first two volumes of the revision are *Electrons and Waves* (1964) and *Quantum Electronics* (1965).

It was the author's plan to confine the revision to two volumes, but inclusion of much new material and a fresh approach to various topics that needed updating from the original publication made a division into three parts more orderly. While each of the three volumes is a self-contained book, the reader should be advised that his enjoyment and understanding will be enhanced if he reads all three in proper sequence.

Dr. Pierce through most of his productive career has been associated with the Bell Laboratories and is one of America's outstanding electronic engineers. He was born on March 27, 1910, at Des Moines, Iowa. From boyhood interested in mathematics, electric circuitry, and vacuum tubes, he received his B.S. in 1933 from the California Institute of Technology. The M.S. followed in the next year and the Ph.D. in 1936, also from Caltech. He joined Bell Labs after receiving the doctorate.

Dr. Pierce's professional career has taken him into many fields of investigation, radio, electronics, acoustics and vision, mathematics, computation, and psychology.

He has been Executive Director, Research-Communications Sciences Division, at Bell. An analysis he made in 1954 led directly (if not smoothly) to the 1960 launching of Project Echo, the forerunner of Telstar, the opening signal for the age of international communication by satellite. He received the National Medal of Science in 1963.

Dr. Pierce credits the science fiction of Jules Verne, H. G. Wells, and Hugo Gernsback with having excited his interest in science, and he himself has composed in the genre, under the nom de plume "J. J. Coupling." His serious writing includes, besides *Electrons, Waves and Messages, Theory and Design of Electric Beams* (Van Nostrand, 1949); *Traveling Wave Tubes* (Van Nostrand, 1950); *Man's World of Sound,* in collaboration with Edward E. David, Jr. (Doubleday, 1958); *Waves and the Ear,* in collaboration with Willem A. van Bergeijk and Edward E. David, Jr. (Science Study Series, 1960); *Symbols, Signals and Noise* (Harper & Row, 1961), and many articles in general magazines and technical journals.

He has received the following awards: Eta Kappa Nu, 1942; Morris Liebmann Memorial Prize, 1947; Stuart Ballantine Medal, 1960; Air Force Association H. H. Arnold Trophy, 1962; the Golden Plate Award of the Academy of Achievement, 1962; the Arnold Air Society General Hoyt S. Vandenberg Trophy, 1963; the Waldemar Poulsen Medal, 1963; the H. T. Cedegren Medal, 1964; Cal Tech Alumni Distinguished Service Award, 1966; and the following honorary degrees: D.Eng. from the Newark College of Engineering, 1961; D.Sc. from Northwestern University, 1961; D.Sc. from Yale University, 1963; D.Sc. from Polytechnic Institute of Brooklyn, 1963; D.Sc. from Columbia University, 1965.

Dr. Pierce is a member of the National Academy of

Sciences, the National Academy of Engineering, and the Air Force Association, and a Fellow of the American Academy of Arts and Sciences, the Institute of Electrical and Electronics Engineers, the American Physical Society, the Acoustical Society of America. He is a Kentucky colonel.

JOHN H. DURSTON

Preface

This book includes a good deal of material from the lat-
ter part of my earlier book, *Electrons, Waves and Messages* (Doubleday, 1956), but it contains a lot of new
material, too, and is very different in emphasis.

In reading *Waves and Messages* over I find it a somewhat disturbing alternation of human aspirations and
dry technical facts. In this it faithfully mirrors engineering, which is my profession. The purpose of engineering is to build useful devices and systems; the whole
end of engineering is to serve human purposes. And
yet, those purposes can be served only through technical resources which are not amenable to argument,
which can be invoked only through precise understanding. I suppose I could have written a less mixed book,
but it wouldn't have been a whole book, as I hope that
this one is.

Dr. Albert Rose was good enough to read and com-
ment on Chapter II of this book. I am indebted to Dr.
W. H. Pickering and Dr. D. Schneiderman of the Jet
Propulsion Laboratory for data on the communication
equipment of the Mariner space probe. I am also much
indebted to a number of my colleagues at the Bell
Telephone Laboratories for corrections and suggestions.
Mr. R. H. Klie kindly went over the whole book very
carefully. Mr. F. J. Kerr, Mr. W. G. Hensel, and Mr.
J. L. Merrill were also most helpful. Further, the pres-

ent book draws heavily on *Transmission Systems for Communication,* by Members of the Technical Staff of the Bell Telephone Laboratories (Revised Third Edition, Bell Telephone Laboratories, Inc., 1964). John H. Durston of Educational Services Incorporated has been most helpful in ways ranging from philosophy to details of presentation.

Miss Florence M. Costello and Miss Elizabeth La Jeunesse were most helpful in typing the book, having the figures prepared, and taking care of other wearing details.

Contents

The Science Study Series   vii

Biographical Foreword   ix

Preface   xiii

CHAPTER I.   Communication Is for People   1

CHAPTER II.   Picking Up Television   19

CHAPTER III.   Signals and Channels   41

CHAPTER IV.   Communication Theory   65

CHAPTER V.   Communication through Space   86

CHAPTER VI.   The Real Challenge   105

APPENDIX I.   Decibels   123

APPENDIX II.   Waves and Frequencies   126

APPENDIX III.   Frequency Shifting   128

Index   130

Waves and Messages

CHAPTER I

Communication Is for People

When I was a boy, in the early days of broadcasting, I built crystal and electron tube radio receivers. I loved to tinker with them, even though I didn't fully understand them. Perhaps a sense of wonder and mystery contributed to my fascination.

The wonder and mystery have not disappeared with the years; they have been pushed deeper, and the curiosity has not been lost. But something has been added—the fascination of *why* as well as *how*. In those days I cared more about picking up a distant station—DX, it was called—than I did about what I heard. I was interested in the phenomenon of radio, not in its purpose. Today, I am astonished that a vast organization of electronic equipment has been built to serve man, and that it has been adapted carefully to his use.

For instance, the common-carrier communication facilities of the United States, which transmit tele-typewriter, voice, data, and television signals, have a capital value of around thirty billion dollars. These facilities exist solely to serve human needs for communication. Moreover, their very nature is dictated by the physical nature and capabilities of human beings.

The teletypewriter keyboard is adapted to the human hand, and the speed of transmission (from sixty to one hundred words a minute) is neither so slow as to be exasperating nor so fast as to be wastefully beyond the speed of an average operator. The telephone provides a loudness, a ratio of signal to noise, and a range of frequencies sufficient to transmit intelligible human speech of acceptable quality. Program circuits, which transmit radio programs and the voice part of television programs, have greater bandwidth and less noise. In television the detail must be fine enough or the picture will appear unduly blurred, and pictures must be sent in a sequence rapid enough to avoid flicker. Moreover, noise must be low enough in comparison with the signal so that the effect we call *snow* is tolerably small.

Thus, criteria of communication have their source in human capabilities—in our speed of acting, our acuity of hearing and understanding, and in the capabilities and limitations of sight. A science fiction writer who invents a world of telepathic protoplasmic blobs will have no place in his story for a teletypewriter, which his characters don't need and couldn't operate. Perhaps life is possible on an airless planet, but with no atmosphere to carry the sound telephony isn't. Removed to the moon, a telephone system would be mute and meaningless, even if all its parts functioned perfectly. And, a "blind" creature who "saw" by radar or smell would have no use for our television with its human standards of performance. He would require a different sort of communication, which would depend on different transmitting and receiving devices, and presumably would have different requirements for bandwidth and noise.

I am afraid that when I was young I either ignored this human aspect of communication or took it for granted, as men for thousands of years have taken speech for granted. The early Greeks could imagine that Prometheus gave man fire, and taught him arts and letters, but man spoke by nature—and indeed, until the Tower of Babel, we are told, all men spoke one tongue.

Today scientists are becoming acutely aware of man's capabilities and limitations—and of their own ignorance concerning them. Experimental psychologists and neurophysiologists work hard to understand, as well as to measure, our ability to see and hear and speak. Psychologists, linguists, and computer experts strive to puzzle out the structure and function of language, and to gain a knowledge that may enable machines to generate and use English text or speech, and perhaps to translate from one language into another.

But in the early days of communication human senses and capabilities were not studied systematically, nor were machines well adapted to human needs. Semaphore telegraphs of the first half of the nineteenth century extended from Prussia to Petrograd and from Berlin to Trier. A hundred and twenty towers dotted hilltops along the 425 miles between Paris and Toulon. A sending operator set large arms in a position representing a particular signal; the receiving operator descried the signal with a spyglass, and repeated it, so that it could be seen at the next

3

station. It took about a minute to send one signal. Either because of the primitive technology, or because of inadequate design, communication by semaphore was slow compared with what we think of as human capabilities and needs, although it was a marvel of its day.

When Samuel F. B. Morse conceived his electric telegraph in 1832, he was still far from adapting electric current and the electromagnet to apt human use. One element remained constant throughout his work—the idea of signaling by making or breaking an electric circuit, and thus causing an electromagnet at a distance to move an iron armature. But the method of making and breaking the current was modified, and so was the task of the electromagnet.

In Morse's first device the current was turned on and off by moving a pattern of metal pegs set in "portrule" past an electric contact. At the receiving end the magnet pressed a stylus against a moving paper while the current flowed, so that the pattern of pegs on the portrule was reproduced on the paper as a sequence of short lines.

To compose a message, Morse assigned numbers to words. At the sending end the operator had to look up the number corresponding to each word; he then transmitted the number by means of the portrule. At the receiving end the operator interpreted the marks on his tape as a number, and looked up the corresponding word.

This early form of telegraphy was clumsy and slow. It was only after Alfred Vail became associated with Morse that several substantial and important improvements were made. During Morse's association with Vail, the Morse code was devised. This system represents letters *and* numbers by appropriate combinations of dots (currents of short duration), dashes (currents of longer duration), and spaces (no current). This ingenious and very efficient code uses short combinations of dots and dashes for frequently occurring letters—one dot for *e,* for instance—and longer codes for less frequently occurring letters. Unlike tables of numbers corresponding to words, the Morse code can be learned by heart.

Two other advances of this period made telegraphy much more apt for human use. One improvement was in reception of the signal. It was found that the receiving operator did not have to read the marks on the paper; he preferred merely to listen to the clicks the apparatus made as the magnet attracted and released the armature. Thus, a simple *sounder,* without a stylus and moving tape, was found to be better adapted to human use than the earlier receiving device. Further, it was found that the proper on-off sequence of current could be produced by operating a simple switch or telegraph *key,* rather than by moving the clumsy portrule past a contact.

The Morse code, the key, and the sounder greatly increased the speed and ease of telegraphy. The advance did not come from more rapid or reliable electrical functioning. Rather, the code, key, and sounder enabled a human being to make more effective use of the electric current and the electromagnet with its armature, which from the start formed the basis of electric telegraphy.

The telegraph code is a man-made alphabet which

we can use in place of roman letters and arabic numerals. The key stands in place of the pen, and we read by ear from a sounder rather than by eye from a page. It is a triumph of human ingenuity that the telegraph worked as well as it did, for it required the user to learn a new alphabet, and new skills of hand and ear.

The telephone is at once simpler and more powerful. It reproduces the human voice; to use it we need merely speak and hear. And in essence, a telephone seems simple indeed. The transmitter consists of a thin metal diaphragm which can respond accurately to the rapidly varying pressure of the sound wave of our speech. The vibrating diaphragm changes the pressure on a little pinch of shiny carbon granules, and this variation changes the electrical resistance between two terminals to which a steady voltage is applied. When we talk into the transmitter, we produce a fluctuating electric current. This current goes through the electromagnet of a receiver and makes the electromagnet attract a thin diaphragm with a force proportional to the current. Thus, the diaphragm of the receiver reproduces the motions of the diaphragm of the transmitter, and hence reproduces the sound wave which caused the diaphragm of the transmitter to vibrate.

It astonished everyone, even Alexander Graham Bell (who knew how faint speech is), that the telephone worked at all. Yet from the very beginning it transmitted a weak but natural voice. Prior to the perfection of the electron tube and its use as an amplifier in long-distance circuits, the sound was weak indeed, and the telephone could not span the continent. With the coming of amplification, problems arose. A louder signal, a broader band of signals, a lower noise would cost more. Was one to strive for perfection, or only to do well enough? And what was "well enough"?

Shortly following World War I, Harvey Fletcher and his colleagues at the Bell Telephone Laboratories started a comprehensive program to explore this question, a program that initiated modern psychoacoustics. This is a tricky field of study, and measurements concerning individual and "average" human beings are continually being revised and improved. But, with the warning that the numbers I shall quote don't represent final truth, I think that it will be interesting to discuss a few of the things that have been learned.

Some of these have to do with the general nature of hearing. How faint sounds can we hear? How intense must a sound be so that we "feel" it? (We may feel it painfully!) Using equipment developed by Fletcher and his colleagues, the U. S. Public Health Service conducted a general survey of the acuity of hearing of a typical American group. The results are shown in Fig. 1.

One of the vertical scales at the left of Fig. 1 is labeled "Intensity Level (decibels)." This gives us an opportunity to become acquainted with a term we will use many times in this volume. The decibel is a measure of the ratio of two powers. If the powers are P_1 and P_2, P_1 is said to be greater than P_2 by $10 \log_{10} (P_1/P_2)$ decibels or db.* We see in Fig. 1,

---

* I have tried to explain decibels more fully in Appendix I.

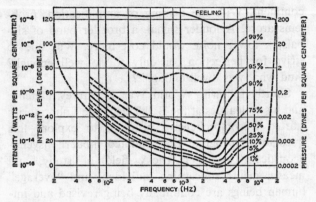

Figure 1

for instance, that a sound intensity of 10^{-14} watt/cm^2 is 20 db greater than a sound intensity of 10^{-16} watt/cm^2.†

Let us now turn to the content of Fig. 1. We see that most people can hear sounds over a frequency range from below 100 cycles‡ to over 8000 cycles. We also see that the sensitivity of the ear varies greatly with frequency. The ear is most sensitive for

† These are the familiar watts used to measure electric power, used here to measure the power of a sound wave. The power of sound striking a large wall is greater than the power striking a small part of it, so the appropriate measure for the intensity of a sound wave is power density—watts/cm^2, that is, watts per square centimeter.

‡ In any periodic (that is, exactly repeated) motion there is a complete *cycle* of change, from start through the particular and repeated motion, and back to start again. In waves, for example, the cycle is from crest through trough and back to crest. The number of *cycles per second* is the *frequency*. For a fuller discussion see the author's *Electrons and Waves*, pages 96–97.

8

frequencies around 3000 cycles. For a 100-cycle sound to be just audible it must be about 5000 times as powerful as the faintest 3000-cycle sound we can hear.

We also see that the sensitivity of the ear varies among individuals. For over 50 per cent of the group tested, the faintest sound that could be heard was twenty or more times as powerful as the faintest sound which could be heard by those with the sharpest hearing.

Our sense of hearing is only one aspect of spoken communication. Another is the nature of speech. The frequency distribution of the power of speech is important. Fletcher made measurements of sound pressures 30 centimeters (cm) from the lips of a talker in each successive octave (at low frequencies) or half octave (at higher frequencies). In Fig. 2 the

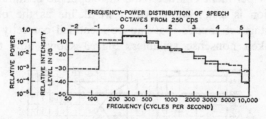

Figure 2

horizontal solid bars are for men's voices; they give the sound power in each band as db below the average power for speech as a whole. The broken bars are for women's voices.

Fig. 1 tells us that the ear is most sensitive around 3000 cycles. But Fig. 2 tells us that the energy of

9

speech is most intense around 300 to 500 cycles. Thus, the frequencies that are most important in spoken communication are not necessarily those to which the ear is most sensitive.

The data given in Figs. 1 and 2 are important to a general understanding of speech and hearing. More particular and pointed data were necessary for the design of a telephone system. One vital question which had to be settled concerned the bandwidth or range of frequencies which a telephone should transmit. The telephone is a utilitarian device; we want to be able to understand what is said over it. When we hear a sentence in a noisy room we can often guess at the meaning, even when we do not get all the individual sounds. But sometimes we can't guess, and it seems best to insist that with the telephone we should grasp individual sounds.

A pertinent characteristic in telephonic communication is *articulation,* which we define as the percentage of sounds that can be identified correctly in spoken nonsense syllables. Fig. 3 shows how the

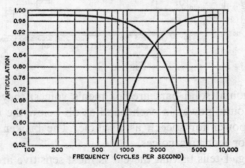

Figure 3

articulation varies as we cut off the lower frequencies in speech (curve which slopes down toward right) or the higher frequencies in speech (curve which rises up toward right).

In telephony, frequencies from about 200 cycles to about 3200 cycles are transmitted. We see from Fig. 3 that this range should result in very little degradation in articulation. Still, a friend of mine finds it hard to convey his initials, *F.K.,* over the telephone; hearers often think he says *S.K.* Before numbers replaced the first two letters of a telephone exchange name, people who called Information sometimes had trouble understanding the two letters. The telephone is good enough, but it is not perfect.

We also need to know how loud a signal supplied to telephone subscribers should be. Here we are not concerned so much with intelligibility as with the preference of the subscriber. In Fig. 4 we have at the bottom the level of the speech signal supplied to a standard telephone set, measured in *vu* (volume units) as read with a *vu meter.* The curves show the percentage of people who judged a given level to be poor or worse, too low to be good, and too high to be good. We see that a level of around −28 vu satisfied everyone, and the region between −20 vu and −35 vu is quite acceptable.

Noise can be an annoyance, and too much noise can *mask* speech, rendering it unintelligible. But we have seen from Fig. 1 that the ear is not equally sensitive to all frequencies, nor is it equally annoyed by noises of all frequencies. Hence, in telephony, noise is measured with a device which is less sensitive to low and high frequencies than to the fre-

11

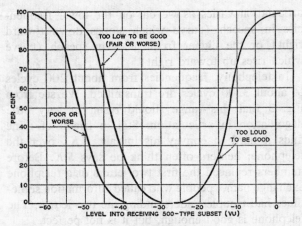

Figure 4

quencies most important in understanding speech. This sensitivity is shown in Fig. 5. At the bottom we have frequency in cycles. Vertically we have a *weighting factor* expressed in decibels. We see that the noise weighting factor for 300 cycles is about −20 db. This means that in measuring noise with a

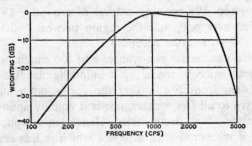

Figure 5

12

noise measuring set, the power of noise of a frequency of 300 cycles is counted only 1/100 as much as the power of noise having a frequency of 1000 cycles.

It takes a surprisingly and annoyingly large amount of noise to reduce the articulation, the intelligibility of speech. Hence, the level of acceptable noise is generally set on the basis of annoyance. In Fig. 6, we have at the bottom the noise power applied to the same telephone set used in establishing Fig. 4. In Fig. 6 the noise power is measured in *dbrnc*. This is db with respect to a 1000 cps single frequency *reference power* of 10^{-12} watt.

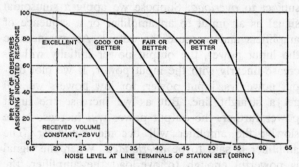

Figure 6

The left-hand curve of Fig. 6 shows the fraction of users who judge a phone with a particular noise to be quiet enough to be excellent. The next curve to the right shows the fraction of users who will judge the phone with a particular noise to be good or better, and so on. Thus, if the noise applied to a

13

phone is 24 dbrnc, 80 per cent of users will judge it to be excellent, and almost all will judge it to be good.

People who design communication systems have to deal with the ratio of signal power to noise power. Fig. 4 shows us that a volume level of −28 vu, which is typical of telephony, is eminently satisfactory. Speech rises and falls rapidly in power. A level of −28 vu corresponds to an *average* power during speaking of about 61 dbrnc. Thus if the noise is 24 dbrnc, the average signal power is greater than *properly weighted* noise (see Fig. 5) by about 37 db.

We are still far from the knowledge of speech and speakers which would enable us to design a perfect communication system. Communication systems are subject to *overload*. Suppose we apply a sinusoidal signal as an input to an amplifier or a sequence of amplifiers and measure the output. As we increase the input power, the output power initially will increase linearly with the input power. If we plot output power vs. input power, for low powers we will get a straight line. But as we increase the input power further, the output power will increase more slowly; the amplifier will become *nonlinear*. The amplifier is said to be *overloaded*. When the signal is powerful enough to overload the amplifier, the output voice signal will be *distorted*. This is bad enough if we are sending one voice signal through the amplifier, but it can become even worse.

In most transmission systems an amplifier is used to amplify many voice signals. The frequency division multiplex, for instance, depends on a device called a *modulator* to shift the frequencies of voice signals. In a multichannel system a number of voice signals, each including frequencies from 200 to 3200 cycles, will be transmitted at frequencies lying in the ranges 64,000 to 68,000 cycles; 68,000 to 72,000 cycles; 72,000 to 76,000 cycles; and so on. In such a system overloading and nonlinear distortion cause *interchannel interference*. Frequencies from one channel are transferred to other channels.

Thus, overloading must be avoided. If we are to avoid overload, we must know not only the average power of a talker's signal, but the peak power of a number of talkers talking at once, and, indeed, how many talkers are talking at once. Of course, there are not precise answers to any of these questions, but we can give satisfactory statistical answers.

Not all channels in a multichannel multiplex system are in use at once. Moreover, channels in multiplex systems transmit speech in one direction only; a long-distance telephone conversation uses up two channels, one in each direction. Thus one channel isn't used when a subscriber is listening rather than talking. In all, during the *busy hour* or time when the system is most heavily used, only about one-fourth of the channels carry speech at any moment.

The power of speech varies from talker to talker, and sometimes we can have a group of loud talkers. We can allow enough power per talker to take this into account. But the speech power of a talker also varies while he is talking; *s* is a weak sound, *o* is a strong one. In the speech of one talker the peak power will be much greater than the average power. But when we consider many talkers together, some will be loudest while others are softest. The data on

15

this effect are quite complicated, but the curve shown in Fig. 7 represents the effect roughly. Here the ratio r of peak to average power, measured in db, is plotted as a function of the number N of channels in the system (the number of *active* channels is only about $N/4$).

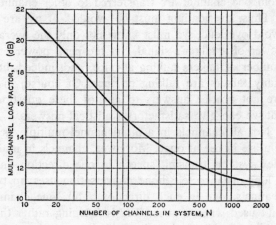

Figure 7

Perhaps an example of all these considerations is in order.

A transmission system used to transmit telephone speech over very long distances may carry 1860 speech signals combined by frequency division multiplex. At some reference point in the system we may find that the average power of one talker *while talking* is -11 dbm (db with respect to one milliwatt). The average number of active channels is $1860/4 = 465$. Thus, the average total power will be

465 times the average power per talker. Or, we can express this power ratio in db and say

$$10 \log_{10} 465 = 26.7 \text{ db}$$

The total average power is about 27 db greater than the average power per speaker. Thus, the total average power in dbm is

$$-11 + 27 = 16 \text{ dbm}$$

We still have to allow for the peak power. From Fig. 7 we see that for 1860 channels the peak power is about 11 db greater than the average power. Thus, the system would have to be capable of transmitting a peak power of about

$$16 + 11 = 27 \text{ dbm}$$

From our earlier consideration of noise, we know that transmission will be excellent if the noise power in each telephone channel, active or inactive, is 37 db less than the average signal power. A usual standard for long-distance circuits is that the noise per channel at the same point we have chosen for the signal be −48 dbm. As the average talker power is −11 dbm, this will give a ratio of average signal power to noise power for the average talker of

$$37 \text{ db}$$

Of course, an appreciable amount of noise will be added in circuits to and from a long-distance transmission system.

It may seem that we have been led into rather abstract matters. But all this calculation can be traced back to the behavior of human beings and the nature of human speech and hearing, as expressed in Figs. 1 to 7. Such data are necessary in order to bridge the gap between the sorts of measurements we can conveniently make on a communication system and the needs and preferences of the human beings who will use such a communication system.

The example of telephony seems a very simple one. The sound pressure of speech varies just as an electric current in a wire can vary. By means of a very simple device, a diaphragm that can vibrate with a sound wave and an electromagnet, Alexander Graham Bell could both transmit and receive intelligible speech. Yet we have seen something of what we need to know about speech in order to design a modern communication system which will transmit speech satisfactorily.

In television the problem at the outset seemed far more difficult, for a picture of a scene is not at all analogous to a current in a wire. In the next chapter we will consider some of the problems of picking up television.

CHAPTER II

Picking Up Television

The inventor of the telegraph was faced with the problem of finding an electrical signaling means which human beings could easily learn to use, and could use easily after learning. The inventor of the telephone was faced with the problem of translating the faint fluctuations of a sound wave into the fluctuations of an electric current, and translating these fluctuations of current back into sound again. The problem of television—of the transmission of sequences of pictures—is in many ways more complicated than either.

As in telephony, we must deal with the extreme keenness of the human senses. As the ear responds to sounds of extremely low power, so the eye can see scenes which are very poorly illuminated. But beyond this, the eye does not see a time sequence of light and dark, but a two-dimensional pattern of light and dark. Such a pattern does not correspond directly to the sort of fluctuating electric current we are familiar with in telegraphy and telephony. It would be hopeless to try to convey pictorial information to a person merely as a time sequence of changing sound or flashing light.

In order to give a human being the effect of sight

19

at a distance, we must in some way adapt electrical signaling to the visual sense. It is the purpose of this chapter to show how this adaptation has been accomplished, and how the obstacles in the way have been overcome.

One general method of transmitting a picture is to break it up into a number of different signals which, taken together, describe the picture with sufficient accuracy to satisfy the eye. In principle, we could derive a group of descriptive signals from a picture in many quite different ways. In principle again, the signals so derived could be transmitted simultaneously over many circuits, or sequentially over one transmission path. As a matter of fact, picture transmission has been achieved by breaking the picture up into small, contiguous *picture elements* and transmitting signals specifying the brightness of such picture elements sequentially over one transmission path. Thus, in sending a single TV picture we in effect send in succession many signals—signals to describe the light or shade of each small part of the picture. How has this been done?

The general scheme that is used in modern television was invented by Paul Gottlieb Nipkow in 1884. Nipkow was unable to achieve television of any sort in his time, chiefly because he did not have amplifiers, but also because he lacked other devices as well. He did contribute two things, however: an idea of how a picture could be transmitted electrically, and a conception of devices that could be used.

How does the picture on your TV screen get there? It is painted on the screen by a fine electron beam which scans across the phosphor on the inside of the face of the picture tube. When the electrons strike the phosphor, it glows with a brightness proportional to the rate at which electrons strike the phosphor; that is, proportional to the current of the electron beam. The TV signal controls this current by means of an electrode near the cathode, just as the voltage on the grid controls the electron current in a triode. Thus, as the beam scans a pattern on the phosphor, it paints the picture repeatedly in light and shade, a complete picture 30 times every second.

This rate, 30 times a second, is not arbitrary. The nature of human vision dictated the choice. We know from the movies that pictures presented sequentially can give the illusion of motion if the presentation is rapid enough. If the presentation is too slow, motion is jumpy. Further and worse, too slow a presentation results in an extremely annoying flicker.

The path of the bright spot which the electron beam produces on the face of the picture tube is shown, rather roughly, in Fig. 8. The beam scans

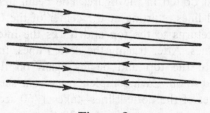

Figure 8

across the picture in the zigzag pattern shown by the solid line. It scans from the left slanting down toward the right; then it quickly returns to the left and scans again to the right, and so on. The rightward motion is properly called the scan. During this motion the beam is turned on and paints out a line of the picture. The quick leftward motion is called the retrace; during this motion the beam is turned off.

Thus, actual lines of the pattern painted on the face of the picture tube appear only during the left-to-right scan, as shown in Fig. 9. The picture is

Figure 9

made up of two interlaced sets of these lines, shown solid and dotted in the figure. The beam first traces the solid lines, starting at the center of the top, and then it returns to the top and traces the interleaved dotted lines. After tracing the dotted lines, the beam returns to the top and begins again on the solid lines, and so on. Each complete trace—one set of lines or one set of the dotted lines—takes 1/60 second, so the whole pattern is traced out 30 times a second.

You may wonder why the picture should be scanned twice with interlaced lines instead of once, going from one line directly to the adjacent line. Interlaced scanning is used to avoid the flicker which would be observed if an appreciable area of the picture were illuminated only 30 times a second, instead of 60 times a second as with interlaced scanning.

There are two chief problems associated with the transmission of television. One is that of synchronization; the beam has to get to the right spot on the receiving tube at the right time. It wouldn't do to have the electron beam paint the upper right-hand corner of the transmitted picture on the center of the receiver picture tube. I thought of explaining the features of the television signal which make synchronization possible, but I found some of the details rather confusing myself. I will say only that at the end of each scan from left to right the transmitter emits a special pulse which tells the receiver to return the electron beam to the left-hand side of the picture tube. Another special pulse is sent out at the end of a complete interlaced scan of the entire picture; this tells the receiver when to move the beam from bottom to top. The synchronizing effect of these special pulses is averaged over many scanning periods in order to minimize the "jitter" caused by noise.

More difficult is the complicated technique of generating a signal that will correspond to the brightness of the scene to be transmitted. The difficulty here arises chiefly because there are so many little parts of the scene which must be described separately, and because there is so little time to describe each one.

The scanning process divides the picture into a total of 525 lines. As the beam moves along each line, it paints out approximately 500 independent patches of light or shade; each patch is called a picture element. In each thirtieth of a second, the television pickup device has to send out signals corresponding to the brightness of about 250,000 different picture elements. At the receiver the picture tube has to paint in these 250,000 distinct patches of light and shade 30 times a second. The time allowed for each picture element is thus about 10^{-7} second. To evaluate the brightness of an element of a picture in this time is really difficult. How difficult it is we can see by a few simple calculations.

To make any calculation we need to know a little about the device which picks up television signals. The earliest device proposed for television pickup used the Nipkow disk, as shown in Fig. 10. This is a

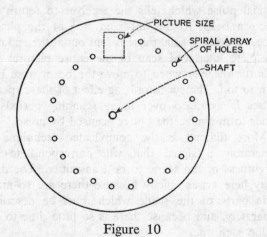

Figure 10

thin disk rotating on a shaft. A spiral pattern of holes is punched through the disk. As the disk rotates, one after another of the holes scans across the picture (the size of the picture is indicated by dotted lines). To scan a picture in an interlaced fashion according to modern TV standards, the disk would have to have 525 holes arranged in two spirals.

Fig. 11 shows a television pickup system using a

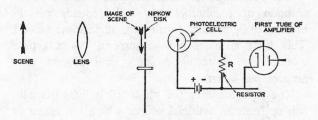

Figure 11

Nipkow disk. The lens produces an image of a scene right on the rotating surface of the Nipkow disk. Thus, the rotating disk lets through light from one little part of the image at a time. This light falls on a photoelectric cell which produces an electric current corresponding to the intensity of the light.

A photoelectric cell consists of a sensitive photo-cathode, which emits electrons when light falls on its surface. The current of electrons, picked up by another electrode, flows through a resistor, *R;* thus, it produces a voltage drop across the resistor *R,* and this voltage acts as the input to an amplifier, of which the first tube only is indicated in Fig. 11.

The signal produced by the current flowing from the photocell through the resistor *R* must compete with a sort of noise due to thermal agitation of electric charges in the resistor. This *Johnson noise* is

25

unavoidable. If the current is not large enough, the signal will be lost in the noise. How large is the signal likely to be? To know this, we must understand something of the intensity of ordinary light and something of the sensitivity of photocells.

The current of electrons released from the photocathode of a photoelectric cell depends on the amount of light which falls on the surface per second. This light is measured in lumens. As a typical example, a photocathode may emit around 10^{-4} ampere per lumen.

The light reaching the photocell is light from the sun or from an artificial source which has fallen on an object and been partially reflected. The intensity of the light falling on an object is measured in foot-candles. For an intensity of one foot-candle the light falling on an object is one lumen per square foot. A standard candle (which was once a real standard of illumination) gives an intensity of one foot-candle at a distance of one foot. The illumination in a room moderately well lighted with incandescent lights may be 40 foot-candles. A room lighted brightly with fluorescent lights may be lighted to an intensity of 100 foot-candles. On a cloudy day the outdoor illumination is around 1000 foot-candles, and sunlight gives an illumination as high as 10,000 foot-candles.

Let us ask how brightly we must illuminate an object in order to get a picture by means of the Nipkow disk device of Fig. 11. Suppose that we call the illumination of the scene L foot-candles. Then L lumens fall on each square foot of the scene. The scene will not reflect all this light. As an estimate, let us say that the scene reflects .24 L lumen per square foot.

The brightness of an image formed by a lens is much less than the brightness of the object which is imaged. For an f/4.5 lens the image is about 1/80 as bright as the scene imaged. Hence, if our TV camera uses an f/4.5 lens, the lumen per square foot in the image will be about 3×10^{-3} L lumen per square foot. How large shall we assume the image of the scene to be? A reasonably convenient size would be three inches by four inches, or 1/12 square foot. For this area, the lumen quantity in the entire image will be about 2.5×10^{-4} L lumen.

However, in order to scan over 250,000 separate elements, the holes in the Nipkow disk must let light pass from only 1/250,000 of the picture at a time. Thus, the light falling through the hole in the Nipkow disk is 10^{-9} L lumen. A reasonable value for the electron current emitted by a photocathode is 10^{-4} ampere per lumen; thus, the total current through the resistance R will be about 10^{-13} L ampere.

The power dissipated in the resistance R is the square of the current times the resistance R. We want to make this value as large as possible. But we cannot make the resistance very large and still amplify as broad a band of frequencies as is necessary in television. A resistance of 2000 ohms is reasonable. For a resistance of 2000 ohms the power dissipated in the resistor because of the photocurrent will be about 2×10^{-23} L^2 watt. We may compare this with Johnson noise power, which is 1.37×10^{-23} TB watt. If the temperature of the resistance, T, is

27

293 degrees Kelvin, and if the bandwidth, B, is 4×10^6 cycles, which is about the bandwidth needed for television, the Johnson noise power will be 1.6×10^{-14} watt.

Suppose that we wish the power due to the photocurrent to be 100 times the Johnson noise power. This ratio would give a good signal. We would have to have

$$\frac{2 \times 10^{-23} \text{ } L^2}{1.6 \times 10^{-14}} = 100$$

$$L = 280,000 \text{ foot-candles}$$

This is over ten times the illumination of direct sunlight! We see one good reason why the system of Fig. 11 is not used for television pickup. There just isn't enough light in the world!

One of the great problems of TV development in the 1930's was to do something about this impossible demand created by the Nipkow disk. One of the persons who took up the problem was Philo T. Farnsworth. The Nipkow disk is a clumsy apparatus. Farnsworth replaced this mechanical system with a purely electronic system. Fig. 12 shows the principal parts of the Farnsworth image dissector tube.

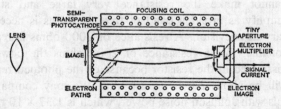

Figure 12

The TV camera lens in his system illuminates a semitransparent photocathode at the left end of the evacuated tube. Voltages applied to electrodes (which are not shown) accelerate the emitted electrons. A longitudinal magnetic field produced by a long focusing coil surrounding the tube focuses the electrons leaving the photocathode, so that an electron image of the scene is reproduced at the point indicated in the tube. This electron image is a sharp reproduction of the scene; the electron current density is large where the scene is bright and small where the scene is dark. Just as a part of the light image passes through an aperture in the Nipkow disk, so a part of the electron image passes through a tiny aperture in a metal sheet and into a device called an electron multiplier.

In the Nipkow disk, you will remember, the aperture moved in order to scan the picture. In the image dissector the entire electron image is shifted past the aperture by means of changing transverse magnetic fields which are produced by deflecting coils not shown in the figure. Because it involves no mechanical motion, the image dissector is more convenient than the Nipkow disk. However, if we merely collected the current of electrons passing through the tiny aperture and fed it to a vacuum tube amplifier, the light required by the image dissector would be the same as that required by the Nipkow disk scanner of Fig. 11.

The real advantage of the image dissector lies in the little box labeled "electron multiplier." In order to understand the advantage, we must explore the contents of this tiny box. The operation of the electron multiplier depends on the fact that when an electron strikes a specially treated metal surface it can knock out several electrons called *secondary electrons*. If the electron striking the surface has been accelerated by a voltage of around 100 volts, it may knock out two to four secondary electrons.

The structure of an electron multiplier is illustrated in Fig. 13. The electrons from the tiny aper-

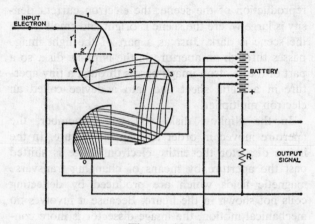

Figure 13

ture of the image dissector strike the first of several specially treated electrodes, marked 1 in the figure. The secondary electrons produced are drawn toward a second electrode, 2, by a fine wire mesh, 2′, which is attached to 2. The battery holds the mesh, 2′, and the second electrode, 2, perhaps 100 volts positive with respect to electrode 1. The secondary electrons leaving electrode 2 are drawn by the mesh

3' to electrode 3, where a further multiplication occurs, and so on. The current of electrons from the final multiplying electrode is collected on an output electrode, 0, and flows through the resistor, *R*, to give an output signal.

By means of an electron multiplier the output current can be made very much greater than the current which passes through the tiny aperture to form the input to the multiplier. For instance, if each multiplying electrode emits three electrons for every electron that strikes it, and if there are 12 multiplying electrodes, then the output current will be about a million times as great as the input current. Such a current is capable of overriding completely the Johnson noise in the resistance *R*.

At first thought, it might seem that this system would solve all our problems, but it does not. What troubles us is the fact that the electron current entering the multiplier consists of tiny but indivisible electrons.

Suppose we assume, just as before, an illumination of L foot-candles. We take the fraction of light reflected to be .24 of the total illumination. We use an f/4.5 lens, giving an image three inches by four inches. The area of the scanning aperture is 1/250,000 of the area of the image; the photocathode emits 10^{-4} ampere per lumen. As before, the current will be 10^{-13} L ampere.

How many electrons per second does this current represent? Current is charge per second. If we divide the current by the charge of the electron, which is 1.6×10^{-19} coulomb (the measure of electric charge), we see that this current constitutes a flow of about 6×10^5 L electrons per second.

In the scanning process we look at each of the 250,000 picture elements 30 times per second. Thus, the time that we devote to examining each element is 1/7,500,000 of a second, or about 1.3×10^{-7} second. How many electrons flow through the tiny aperture in this time? The number is clearly the number of electrons per second multiplied by the time we look at a picture element, about .1 L electron per picture element.

If the average number of electrons per picture element were only one-half, by chance we would sometimes get no electron per picture element, sometimes one, and very infrequently we would get two or three electrons. The signal would be an inadequate representation of the brightness of the scene, because from scan to scan it would fluctuate about the true value and never accurately attain it. The signal would be noisy, and the corresponding picture would have the changing, mottled appearance we call "snow."

To get an accurate representation of the scene, suitable for commercial television, we would need many more electrons per picture element, perhaps a hundred, so that the different brightnesses of different picture elements could be accurately distinguished by different numbers of electrons. Suppose we were to telecast a scene on a cloudy day, when L is about 1000 foot-candles. For the parts of the picture reflecting the assumed fraction .24 of the incident light we would get about 24 electrons per picture element, and this intensity would give a reasonably good picture.

Even on a cloudy day the image dissector would give a usable picture out-of-doors. However, we have made no allowances for imperfections, and actual performance might be inferior to what we have calculated. The image dissector is much more sensitive than the Nipkow disk device, but it is still not good enough for practical TV.

What is the real secret of TV pickup devices? It is the *storage principle,* a contribution of Vladimir K. Zworykin. This principle was first used in a device called the iconoscope. I shall not describe the iconoscope because its operation is inherently complicated and somewhat faulty. Instead, I shall describe a very good as well as an easily understandable pickup tube, the image orthicon.

Fig. 14 shows the principal parts of the image orthicon. Focusing and deflecting coils and many of the electrodes are omitted in the drawing. At the extreme left, the light image falls on a photocathode. The emitted electrons are accelerated by a piece

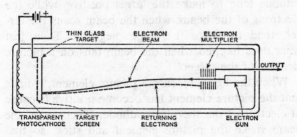

Figure 14

33

of very fine mesh called a target screen. Just beyond the target screen is an extremely thin glass target. The electrons from the photocathode are focused on this target.

When the accelerated electrons from the photocathode pass through the target screen and strike the target beyond, they knock out secondary electrons. Negative electrons leave the target, and the target tends to get more positive as time passes. Where the image is bright, more secondaries leave the target; where the image is weak, fewer electrons leave the target.

An electron beam from an electron gun scans the target. This electron beam strikes the opposite (the right-hand) side of the target, but the electrons strike so gently that they do not knock out many secondary electrons. Hence, the electrons tend to stick and, where the beam strikes, make the target negative.

The target is extremely thin, and no insulator is perfect. Thus, the target behaves as if both sides were connected electrically. At a given picture element on the target the electrons from the photocathode tend to make the target positive, while the electrons of the beam, when the beam scans the target, tend to make the target negative. Then just what does happen when the beam falls on a picture element of the target?

When the beam reaches a picture element, it finds that the picture element has become positive because of electrons from the photocathode. Electrons of the beam strike the picture element and stick, so that the picture element becomes more negative. Finally, the picture element becomes so negative that it repels all further electrons in the beam that try to reach it. In effect, the picture element abstracts a certain number of electrons from the beam while the beam falls on it.

How many electrons does the picture element abstract from the beam? Just as many as were knocked out of the other side of the target by electrons from the photocathode. Hence, the number of electrons that a given element of the target abstracts from the beam is an accurate measure of the brightness of the image on the corresponding portion of the photocathode.

The electrons of the beam that are not abstracted by the target are reflected. They go to an electron multiplier, and the output current of the multiplier forms the signal output of the image orthicon. Because a bright portion of the image abstracts many electrons from the beam, the output current will be weak for bright portions of the image and strong for dark portions of the image, but in this upsidedown fashion the beam current faithfully reproduces the brightness of the image.

To find out why the image orthicon is superior to the image dissector, we must know how many electrons a given picture element abstracts from the beam. This is a number governed by the number of electrons which fell on the picture element from the target in the period of 1/30 second since the beam last scanned the picture element. In effect, each picture element of the target remembers all the electrons which reached it from the photocathode in the 1/30 second since it was last scanned by the beam. The image dissector uses only the electrons emitted by a picture element of the photocathode during the time it is being scanned; this period is only 1/250,000 as long as the time between scans.

The limiting sensitivity of the image orthicon is governed by the number of electrons leaving a picture element of the photocathode in 1/30 second. The photocathode is rather small; the total image occupies perhaps 2×10^{-2} square foot, and a picture element occupies 1/250,000 of this, or about 8×10^{-8} square foot. If the illumination is L foot-candles, and if a fraction .24 of the light is reflected, the reflected light will be, as before, .24 L lumen per square foot. If we use an f/4.5 lens, the illumination at the image will be, as before, 3×10^{-3} L lumen per square foot. As the area of the picture element is 8×10^{-6} square foot, the light per picture element will be 2.4×10^{-8} L lumen. If the photocathode gives 10^{-4} ampere per lumen, the current per picture element will be 2.4×10^{-12} L ampere. As the charge of an electron is 1.6×10^{-19} coulomb, the number of electrons per picture element per second will be 1.5×10^7 L electrons per second. The number of electrons which leave an element between scans is 1/30 of this, or 5×10^5 L electrons per scan.

If we took this computation literally, we would believe that an image orthicon could pick up a good picture with an illumination of a thousandth of a foot-candle—that is, the light provided by a single candle at a distance of 30 feet!

The image orthicon is not this good; there are sources of noise we have not taken into account. However, it will pick up a fair picture by the illumination of a candle three feet away (1/9 foot-candle), and a recognizable picture can be obtained with an illumination of a few thousandths of a foot-candle, if a somewhat faster lens than the f/4.5 we have assumed is used. Of course, the image orthicon ordinarily is used with much higher illumination to obtain TV pictures of commercial quality.

In the Nipkow disk device the limitation is Johnson noise in the resistor across the input of the amplifier. The image dissector also has its limitation: in order to give a good picture, a fair number of electrons must be emitted per picture element while the picture element is being scanned (during 1/7,500,000 second). In the image orthicon the limitation lies in the fact that a fair number of electrons must be emitted per picture element in the time between scans (in 1/30 second).

Is it possible to make a better pickup tube than the image orthicon? Fundamentally, the answer seems to be no. It is possible, however, that certain shortcomings in the performance of the image orthicon might be remedied. For instance, we have assumed that the photocathode gives a current of 10^{-4} ampere per lumen. It is conceivable that a photocathode might give a somewhat higher current. Quantum theory tells us that light comes in little packages of energy called quanta. Conceivably, we might get one electron for each quantum, and this exchange would give a current of around 7×10^{-4} ampere per lumen, and so improve the operation of the image orthicon by a factor of around seven. That, as far as I can see, is as good as could possibly be done.

Present image orthicons fall short of this ideal, not only because the quantum efficiency of the photocathode is less than unity, but also because the electron scanning beam which picks up the signal may not be modulated fully, and the *shot noise* associated with the electrons of the scanning beam may add a noise greater than the signal. In the *image intensifier orthicon,* electron multiplication of the electron flow from the photocathode is used to produce a more intense pattern of charge, which is then scanned. With such tubes good pictures of scenes under illumination of around 10^{-5} foot-candle have been recorded.

Another sort of pickup tube called the *vidicon* rivals the image orthicon in performance. The vidicon makes use of a thin film of light-sensitive semiconductor. Some modern vidicons give about one electron of charge on the surface of the film for each photon of light striking it. Operation of a vidicon under extremely low lighting would require both an image intensifier at the target end and an electron multiplier at the gun end; neither is yet in commercial form.

We have seen that the storage feature of pickup tubes is vital if they are to be useful at reasonable light intensities. Storage can be vitally important in other applications. For instance, when a Tyros satellite takes a picture of the earth, or a Ranger satellite takes a picture of the moon, or a Mariner space vehicle takes a picture of Mars, the "exposure" of the television camera must be short compared with the time required to transmit the picture signal to earth. A short exposure can be achieved with a mechanical shutter. The stored pattern of charge resulting from the exposure, and representing the picture, can be read off by causing the electron beam to scan the charge pattern at a convenient rate; the output signal from the scan can be recorded on magnetic tape, or by other means, for later transmission to earth.

The problems of picking up television have been tackled solely because we have a sense of sight and we want to see at a distance. The number of picture elements is dictated by the acuity of our vision—our sense of what is sharp and what is blurred. The scanning rate and the use of interlace are dictated by the quickness of the eye—its ability to follow motion and its sensitivity to flicker. The tolerable noisiness of the picture—how many electrons we need per picture element—is set by our annoyance at incorrect rendering of light and shade.

The noise or "snow" in television does not arise entirely in the television pickup tube. Some is added in transmission. And, just as the ear is not equally sensitive to noise of all frequencies, so the eye is not equally sensitive to noise of all frequencies. High-frequency noise signals produce very fine grained snow in a picture. The eye is less annoyed by such fine-grained snow than by the coarser-grained, blotchier snow caused by lower-frequency noise. The weighting curve commonly used in comparing the relative importance of noise of various frequencies is shown in Fig. 15. This tells us that a low-frequency noise signal (a frequency around 50 kilocycles) must be 14 db weaker than a 4-megacycle noise signal if the two are to be equally annoying.

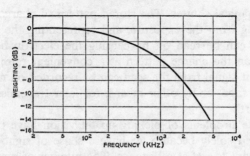

Figure 15

In measuring noise in television transmission circuits, the noise is "weighted" according to the curve of Fig. 15. The high-frequency noise adds much less to the over-all noise reading than low-frequency noise does.

CHAPTER III

Signals and Channels

Until very recent years human beings have generated and received the messages transmitted over communication channels. Today we may have a computer at one or both ends. A communication channel links the message source to the message destination by means of electromagnetic waves which travel along wires, through coaxial cables, through tubes called waveguides, or as radio waves between transmitting and receiving antennas.* In linking voices or pictures to electromagnetic waves we use all sorts of gadgets, including telephone transmitters and receivers, television pickup and picture tubes, transistors, vacuum tubes, inductors, capacitors, and resistors.

The physical nature of the electromagnetic waves we use in telephony is quite different from the physical nature of the sound waves which bring speech to our ears. The light waves of vision are akin to radio waves—both are electromagnetic waves—but this sameness of physical nature is irrelevant in communicating via television.

In both telephony and television we abstract at the transmitting end a pattern characteristic of a humanly interesting phenomenon (voice or picture)

* See *Electrons and Waves*.

41

and impress it on an appropriate electromagnetic wave. At the receiving end we make use of the pattern of the electromagnetic wave in re-creating the humanly interesting phenomenon (voice or picture). The re-creation is never perfectly accurate. This lack of perfect fidelity may be due to limitations or imperfections in the apparatus we use, but it may also be due to random signals called noise which inescapably but inadvertently become mixed up with the electromagnetic waves.

Let us consider this matter more particularly. In Chapter I, we noted that a great many telephone conversations can be made into one combined signal, which can be sent through a single amplifier, over a single pair of wires, or over a single microwave channel. This can be done by a means called frequency-division multiplex. Each of the bands of frequencies about 3000 cycles wide which carry individual voice signals is shifted up in frequency by a different amount. Thus, these bands of frequencies can be stacked one above another in the combined signal.

If we analyzed the way the voltage of the combined signal varied with time, we would find that it had components of many frequencies. By using a filter which passes only a particular band of frequencies, we could select the frequencies corresponding to a particular voice signal, and by shifting these frequencies down to their original values we could recover the original voice signal. If, however, we looked at the voltage at merely one instant of time, we could only say that this voltage was partly due to each voice signal transmitted. We would not have enough information to say, this part of the voltage belongs to talker A, and that part to talker B, and so on. The various parts of the signal could be separated only with filters passing various bands of frequencies.

It is quite different in the case of the television signal, which we discussed in Chapter II. In sending a picture by television we have in effect to send many signals, one for each picture element. If we look at the voltage of the signal representing all these picture elements, we can say the voltage at one particular moment represents the brightness of the 13,878th picture element, and the voltage 1.2×10^{-7} second later will represent the brightness of the 13,879th picture element. We can say further that if a particular voltage represents the brightness of the 13,878th picture element, the voltage exactly 1/30 second later will also represent the brightness of the 13,878th picture element, its new brightness after an interval of 1/30 second.

In television broadcasting the total bandwidth of frequencies transmitted is used in a way very different from the use of a broad band of frequencies in sending many voice signals by means of frequency-division multiplex. In transmitting television we must send a distinct pulse representing the brightness of each picture element. As we send 250,000 picture elements 30 times a second, each pulse can be only about 1/7,500,000 second long. There is a rough rule that the bandwidth must be about 1 divided by the pulse length. This rule tells us that for TV we should need a bandwidth of about 7,500,000 cycles, or 7.5 megacycles. The rule is an approximate one, and does not distinguish between amplitude-modulated waves (which have two different sideband frequencies for each frequency in the modulating signal) and a modulating signal itself. Actually, a bandwidth of 4 megacycles suffices for television.

From the combined frequency-division signal representing many telephone channels we could separate out a single voice signal by means of a filter which would pass or select a certain band of frequencies which carry that voice signal. In merely looking at the voltage of the combined signal at a given instant of time we could not, however, decide which part belonged to one voice signal and which to another. The television signal is also a composite of many signals, one for each picture element. Yet we can look at the voltage of a television signal at a particular instant and say that it corresponds to the brightness of some particular picture element. However, if we filtered a band of frequencies out of the television signal, we would find in this band of frequencies parts representing the brightnesses of all the picture elements.

It is apparent that there is more than one way to send several separate signals through one amplifier, or over one pair of wires, or over one microwave channel. One way is to assign separate bands of frequencies to different signals. This is called frequency-division multiplex. Another is to assign separate, discrete, periodically recurring intervals of time to the different signals. This is called time-division multiplex. As a matter of fact, it can be shown that there is an infinity of other mixed ways of combining and sorting out signals, but the methods of *frequency division* (assigning separate bands of frequency) and *time division* (assigning separate periodically recurring times) are the two practically important methods.

Which is better, frequency division or time division? In attempting to answer such a question we must know some of the limitations of each. Let us consider time division. Suppose our signal is a voltage that varies with time, as in (a) in Fig. 16. Suppose that we want to make measurements on this signal so that a description of it can be sent by time division. The natural thing to do is to measure

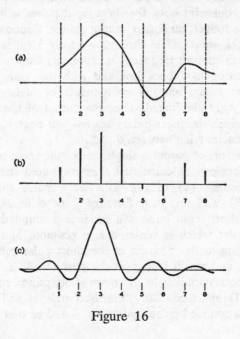

Figure 16

the voltage at regular intervals of time, at 1, 2, 3, 4, . . . , 8, and so on. This is commonly called *sampling* the signal. We could then send these voltages as short pulses of corresponding amplitudes, as shown in (b) of Fig. 16. Such pulses are called *samples* of the signal.

We can see that the short pulses or samples of (b) of Fig. 16 give some sort of description of the signal (a) of Fig. 16. How can we use such a description in terms of a series of short pulses to reconstruct the original signal? To be short, a pulse must contain high frequencies. If we pass the short pulses of (b) of Fig. 16 through a filter which passes low frequencies only, the short input pulses will give rise to longer, smoother output pulses. Suppose we pass the short pulses through a highly idealized filter such that all frequency components from 0 to B pass through without loss and with the same time lag, or delay, and all components of higher frequency are eliminated. Then the output of the filter into which the short pulses are fed will contain only frequencies lying between 0 and B.

The sort of output a single one of the short pulses produces can be calculated. The computed shape is sketched in (c) of Fig. 16. For a pulse spacing $1/(2B)$ and an ideal filter of bandwidth B, the third short input pulse will produce a rounded output pulse which is centered at a position, 3, corresponding to the position of the short pulse producing it, and which is zero at the positions 1, 2, 4, 5, etc., corresponding to the other short pulses spaced $1/(2B)$ apart. Similarly, the short pulse 4 will produce a rounded pulse centered at 4 and zero at 1, 2,

Signals and Channels

3, 5, etc. Thus, all the short pulses together will produce a combined output signal whose amplitude at
position 1 is given entirely by the amplitude of short
pulse 1, whose amplitude at 2 is given only by the
amplitude of the short pulse 2, etc., and which is of
a generally smooth character.

How good a reproduction of the original signal
is this smooth output? It is an exact reproduction of
the original signal at each pulse position, 1, 2, 3,
etc., for the amplitudes at these points are proportional only to the amplitudes of the short pulses
1, 2, 3, and these in turn were obtained from the
original signal. It can be shown mathematically that
the reproduction of the signal is in fact perfect provided that the original signal contains no frequencies
higher than $B!$ We remember that we send $2B$
short pulses per second, and we use a filter of bandwidth B in reproducing the signal. Thus we certainly
couldn't reproduce a signal with a bandwidth greater
than B. Mathematical analysis shows that we can
reproduce perfectly a signal with a bandwidth B or
less.

Suppose we want to send many signals of bandwidth B on a channel which has an over-all bandwidth greater than B. First, we construct a series of
short pulses spaced $1/(2B)$ apart for each channel.
Then we interleave these sets of pulses in time. Fig.
17 shows short pulses from three channels, I, II, and
III, so interleaved. Thus, we have a composite signal
representing three channels, each of bandwidth B.
Pulse I represents the voltage on Channel I at a particular time; II that on Channel II; III that on Chan-

nel III; and I′ that on Channel I again, a period
$1/(2B)$ later than I.

The short pulses of the combined signal in Fig. 17

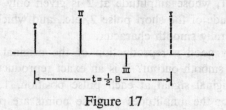

Figure 17

contain very high frequencies. However, we can pass
them all through a filter of bandwidth $3B$. In the
resulting output signal the signal due to I is zero at
II and III; that due to II is zero at I and III; and so
on. Thus, the signals due to the short pulses are by
no means scrambled together, for if we measure the
amplitude of the smoothed-out signal at I we find
the exact amplitude of the short pulse I, etc.

How much total bandwidth have we used to send
three bands each of bandwidth B by time-division
multiplex? We have used a bandwidth of $3B$, just as
we would have had to do in the case of frequency-
division multiplex.

The method and apparatus used to send three
channels of bandwidth B over a single channel of
bandwidth $3B$ is very different in the cases of frequency-division multiplex and of time-division multiplex, as is shown by the comparison in Fig. 18. In
(a) of Fig. 18 we have the components of a
frequency-division multiplex system. Channel II is
shifted in frequency from the band $0 - B$ to the band

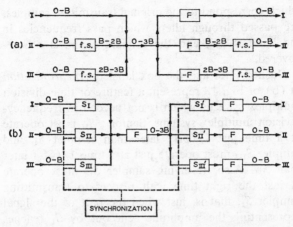

Figure 18

$B - 2B$ by a frequency shifter, *f.s.* Channel III is shifted from $0 - B$ to $2B - 3B$. The three signals are combined and sent over a single channel of band $0 - 3B$. Then the three component channels $0 - B$, $B - 2B$, $2B - 3B$ are separated by filters, F. Channel I is recovered directly and Channels II and III are recovered by frequency shifting.

In doing the same over-all job by time division, as shown in (b) of Fig. 18, Channels I, II, and III are sampled by samplers, S_I, S_{II}, and S_{III} to produce short pulses representing their amplitudes at slightly different times. The interleaved samples are passed through a filter to reduce the bandwidth to $3B$ and are sent over a common channel. At the receiver, the amplitudes of the samples are recovered by sampling the common wave at just the right times by samples S_I', S_{II}', and S_{III}'. The recovered samples,

49

which correspond to the original transmitted samples, are passed through filters which pass frequencies in the band $0 - B$, and the original channels are recovered.

Dashed lines and the box labeled *synchronization* in (b) of Fig. 18 represent a feature of time-division multiplex systems which is not needed in frequency-division multiplex systems. Sampler S_{II} must operate at a time just $1/(6B)$ later than sampler S_I, and sampler S_{III} must operate just at a time $1/(6B)$ later than S_{II}. Also, receiving sampler $S_I{}'$ must operate at just the right time with respect to transmitting sampler S_I; that is, just when the part of the signal representing the amplitude sent out by S_I reaches $S_I{}'$. Synchronization is accomplished at the transmitter or at the receiver by operating the samplers by means of a common driving device. Synchronization between transmitter and receiver is accomplished by sending special, recognizable pulses over the common channel, along with the signal.

Our idealized time-division and frequency-division multiplex systems require just the same bandwidth to send the same number of channels. What about noise? Suppose that in receiving the combined signal the receiver introduces a certain amount of noise. When the channels are separated, this noise is split up differently in the time-division and frequency-division systems, but it is split three ways in each case. If the intensity of the noise is constant with frequency, so that there is the same amount of noise power for each unit bandwidth, in each case the total amount of noise in each recovered channel, I, II, or III, will be the same. Ideal time-division and frequency-division systems require the same bandwidths, and they are equally susceptible to noise.

In discussing noise and bandwidth in connection with frequency division and time division, we have, of course, been indulging in highly idealized thinking. Actually, to transmit three channels of bandwidth *B* by frequency division requires a bandwidth greater than 3*B,* because actual filters are imperfect and cannot sharply distinguish between frequencies lying close together; some *guard band* must be allowed between different frequency channels. Similarly, in time division the ideal shapes of pulses cannot be attained exactly. To avoid mixing up samples, shorter pulses must be sent over the common channel; more bandwidth than the ideal is required.

When we seek a realistic answer to our original question of which is better, frequency division or time division, we get various solutions for various technical reasons. Frequency division is used in telephony to transmit many voice signals over one pair of wires, or one coaxial cable, or one microwave channel, for good but complicated reasons. Television is essentially a time-division transmission of many picture elements. In some microwave military equipment time division is used to transmit several voice channels over one microwave channel. The reasons for choosing between frequency division and time division are much too complicated to discuss here.

We have seen, however, that the fundamental limitations on *ideal* frequency-division and time-division systems are the same, and these limitations show that bandwidth is a very persistent quality. As

Fig. 18 indicates, when we combine signals in very different ways and send them over a common channel, the ideal minimum bandwidth which we need is the sum of the bandwidths of all the individual channels which we send simultaneously.

We might ask whether this is all the bandwidth we ever need to send a signal in a perfectly operating system. The answer is no. When we modulate the amplitude of a radio-frequency wave of frequency f with a voice signal containing frequencies lying in the range $0 - B$, we produce a radio-frequency wave of frequencies lying between $f - B$ and $f + B$; that is, a signal spanning a band $2B$ wide. Amplitude modulation is not an ideal system of transmission, even when the apparatus is ideal and works perfectly.

What about frequency modulation? Suppose that we use FM to send an audio signal with frequencies lying in the band $0 - B$. If in frequency-modulating the radio-frequency wave we swing the frequency back and forth just a little, the bandwidth of the frequency-modulated signal, it can be shown, is $2B$, just as in the case of AM. Suppose, however, that we make the modulating audio signal louder, so that the frequency is swung farther back and forth. This greater moldulation will of course make the received audio signal louder. It will also increase the bandwidth of the frequency-modulated signal which must be transmitted and received. The *index of modulation* is defined as the ratio of the amount of frequency swing above or below the average frequency to the bandwidth B of the signal to be transmitted. When the index is high, the bandwidth needed is about twice the index of modulation times the bandwidth *B* of the audio signal to be transmitted.

If we double the index of modulation, we double the voltage of the received audio signal, and hence we increase its power by a factor 2^2, or four, times. This tends to make the ratio of signal power to noise power greater. The increase is not clear gain, however. If we double the index, we double the bandwidth of the radio signal, and we have to double the bandwidth of the FM radio receiver. As noise power is proportional to bandwidth, this doubling of bandwidth doubles the noise that the receiver adds to the received radio signal. If we make the index of modulation great enough, the noise will become comparable in power to the signal, and the mechanism of demodulation will become inoperative. Up to this "breaking" point, however, most of the noise associated with the additional bandwidth lies outside the bandwidth of the demodulated signal, and for a fixed transmitter power the signal-to-noise power ratio of the demodulated signal is proportional to the square of the index of modulation.

There is, of course, an even more important limitation on the bandwidth than that at which frequency modulation becomes inoperative. The Federal Communications Commission parcels out bandwidth for various purposes. It has only so much to parcel out, and it will not give unlimited amounts for any one purpose. The channel width assigned to one FM station is 150,000 cycles, and this limits the index of modulation which can be used.

It was the late Edwin H. Armstrong who, in 1936, first demonstrated the use of broad-band frequency modulation in reducing noise. The result astounded and confounded radio engineers. Because noise increases with bandwidth, they had always thought that the way to reduce noise in the finally received signal was to limit bandwidth as much as possible everywhere in the transmission system. Armstrong, however, showed that in an FM system one could reduce the noise in the received audio signal by increasing the radio-frequency bandwidth. Clearly, in an over-all transmission system the relation between bandwidth and noise is not as simple as engineers had assumed.

Frequency modulation is only one of many systems in which the over-all effect of noise can be reduced by increasing the bandwidth. In fact, in some systems of transmission the effect of noise added in transmission can be virtually eliminated. These systems use signals which are of the same on-off type as the telegraph signals we discussed in Chapter I.

For instance, consider the signal shown in Fig. 19,

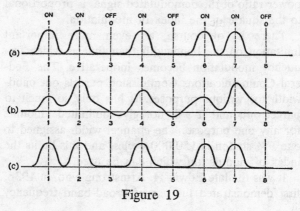

Figure 19

which consists of a sequence of pulses at regular times 1, 2, . . . , 8. At these times the signal must be either *on* or *off;* it can assume no intermediate values. Such a signal, reading *on, on, off, on, off, on, on, off* is shown in (a) of Fig. 19. It is more convenient to write *1* instead of *on* for a pulse and *0* instead of *off* for the absence of a pulse. Thus, the signal of (a) of Fig. 19 may be represented 11010110.

Suppose we add a certain amount of random noise to the signal of (a) of Fig. 19. The amplitude will increase at some *pulse positions* (the times 1, 2, . . . , 8) and decrease at others. Thus, the pulses plus noise may look as shown in (b) of Fig. 19. If, as in the case of (b) of Fig. 19, the noise is not great enough to obliterate the difference between an *off* and an *on,* we can tell whether an *on* or an *off,* a 1 or a 0, was meant, despite the distortion in the pulse pattern caused by the addition of noise. Even with a small amount of noise, a noise peak will sometimes (but very infrequently) cause an error in interpretation. We can make an electronic gadget called a *regenerator* which will examine the signal of (b) of Fig. 19 at each of the times 1, 2, . . . , 8 and decide whether or not there is a pulse present. The regenerator can send out a new, noise-free signal, a clean, uniform pulse if a noisy pulse was present, and no pulse if no pulse was present among the noise. Such a regenerated signal is shown in (c) of Fig. 19; it is indistinguishable from the original signal (a). When our signal can have only certain discrete values, as *off* or *on,* we can almost completely eliminate the effects of noise if the noise is not too large.

In the example, we have eliminated noise effects at the expense of sending not a continuous range of amplitudes but only *on* or *off;* 1 or 0. What is such a signal good for, anyway? For one thing, we could send the letters of the alphabet by means of such signals. We could send pulses in groups of 5 and let different patterns represent different letters. We could, for instance, use the following *code:*

Letter	Code (or pulse pattern)	Letter	Code (or pulse pattern)
a	00001	n	01110
b	00010	o	01111
c	00011	p	10000
d	00100	q	10001
e	00101	r	10010
f	00110	s	10011
g	00111	t	10100
h	01000	u	10101
i	01001	v	10110
j	01010	w	10111
k	01011	x	11000
l	01100	y	11001
m	01101	z	11010

In this case, the three groups of pulses, 1, 2, 3, of Fig. 20 would spell *cat.*

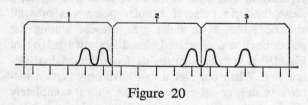

Figure 20

What about voice signals as used in telephony? We can send them by using groups of pulses, too!

We have seen that if we are to send a voice signal with a 4000-cycle bandwidth, we can sample the amplitude of the signal 8000 times a second and send the amplitudes of these samples to the receiver. For instance, (a) of Fig. 21 shows a part of a voice sig-

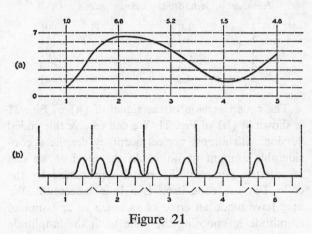

Figure 21

nal whose amplitude lies between 0 and 7. At appropriate sampling times, 1, 2, . . . , 5 the amplitudes (written above) are 1.0, 6.6, etc. Suppose we take as an approximation the amplitude to the nearest units and represent it by the following code:

Amplitude	Code
0	000
1	001
2	010
3	011
4	100
5	101
6	110
7	111

57

If we now allow three pulse positions per sample, we can encode to the nearest digit the amplitudes of the samples of (a) of Fig. 21 as follows:

Sample Number	True Amplitude	Approximate Amplitude	Code
1	1.0	1	001
2	6.6	7	111
3	5.2	5	101
4	1.5	2	010
5	4.6	5	101

The coded version of the signal of (a) of Fig. 21 is shown in (b) of Fig. 21. We can receive this coded version with almost perfect accuracy despite a considerable amount of noise. At the receiver we can reconstruct perfectly the signal represented by the code. But the code itself is a little inaccurate. We may have made an error of as much as $\pm \frac{1}{2}$ unit of amplitude in choosing the code to fit the amplitude as nearly as possible.

The sort of transmission we have just described is called *pulse-code modulation;* the name may be abbreviated PCM. To send a signal of bandwidth B by PCM we sample the signal $2B$ times a second and *encode* the amplitude of each sample as a sequence of n pulses. Thus, we have to transmit $2nB$ pulses per second in sending the signal, and the ideal minimum bandwidth required for such transmission is $nB,$ or n times the bandwidth of the signal to be sent.

In choosing an amplitude to fit the sample, we have a choice of 2^n amplitudes, for there are 2^n different combinations of n ons or offs, taken n at a time. Because these 2^n amplitudes do not fit exactly the signal we want to transmit, the encoding process itself is responsible for a sort of noise called *quantizing* noise, which is the error between the actual signal amplitude and the nearest amplitude provided by the code. Power varies as the square of amplitude. The amplitude of the largest signal we can represent is 2^n times as great as the difference between adjacent amplitudes, and this difference is proportional to the amplitude of the quantizing noise. Hence, we can get some idea of the signal-to-noise power ratio by squaring the number of amplitudes, obtaining $(2^n)^2 = 2^{2n}$. The table below gives some values of 2^{2n} for various numbers n of pulses per sample:

n	2^{2n}
(number of pulses per sample; bandwidth required is nB)	*(the signal-to-noise power ratio is proportional to 2^{2n})*
2	16
4	256
6	4100
8	65,500
10	1,050,000
12	16,800,000

We see that the signal-to-noise ratio increases extremely rapidly with the increase in bandwidth, much more rapidly than for FM. And PCM is almost completely immune to moderate noise in the receiver, although the system itself introduces the quantizing noise we have discussed. If we use eight or ten pulses per sample—that is, eight or ten times the signal bandwidth, *B*—we can reproduce the signal with virtually no noise. For voice transmission very acceptable reproduction is attained using seven pulses per sample. Actual PCM systems commonly use more pulses per sample to avoid undue noise if the signal is encoded and decoded several times in succession.

In order to make our discussion of coded transmission complete, we might ask whether one can *reduce* the bandwidth needed to transmit a signal. A few years ago, if you had asked this of an engineer he would have unhesitatingly said *no,* almost without thinking. But now by thinking just a little, we can see that reduction is indeed possible.

Suppose, for instance, that we want to send the two-valued, on-off signal of bandwidth *B,* shown in (a) of Fig. 22. The signal consists of a distinguish-

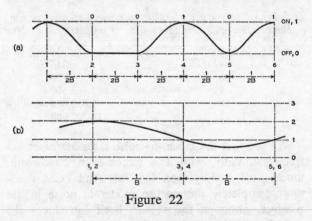

Figure 22

able *on* or *off,* 1 or 0, *pulse* or *no pulse* each $1/(2B)$ seconds. Ordinarily, we would simply transmit this signal as it is, by sending $2B$ zeros or ones, no-pulses or pulses, each second.

However, we can describe the signal accurately by sending only *B* pulses per second, provided that we allow not two different kinds of pulses (amplitudes 0 and 1), but four different kinds of pulses (amplitudes 0, 1, 2, 3). We group the simple $0-1$ pulses we wish to send into pairs and let one of the more complicated four-amplitude pulses describe a pair of the simpler two-amplitude pulses. Thus, we have to send only one complicated pulse for each pair of simple pulses we wish to describe.

We can let four-amplitude pulses represent pairs of two-amplitude pulses according to the following code:

Pair of 2 on-off pulses

Amplitude of first two-amplitude pulse of pair	Amplitude of second two-amplitude pulse of pair	Amplitude of four-amplitude pulse representing pair of two-amplitude pulse
0	0	0
0	1	1
1	0	2
1	1	3

The six pulses of (a) of Fig. 22, and the corresponding codes, are given below:

Numbers of pulses constituting pair	Amplitudes of pulses constituting pair	Amplitude of pulse representing pair
1, 2	10	2
3, 4	01	1
5, 6	01	1

The three four-value pulses corresponding to the six two-value pulses are shown in (b) of Fig. 22. Because we have to send elements of the four-value pulses only half as frequently as we had to send the two-value pulses, we need only half as much bandwidth. Thus, it *is* possible to reduce the bandwidth needed to send a signal, but to do so it is necessary to construct a signal of more distinguishable amplitudes than the original signal had. This makes the signal of reduced bandwidth much more susceptible to noise than was the original signal. Multiple-amplitude pulses have been used in sending more data or encoded voice signals over existing communication channels than could be sent using two-level or binary signals.

Everything in this chapter confirms an impression that bandwidth is extremely important in connection with signals. If we have to send some number, N, of channels, each of bandwidth B, we can shift the frequencies of these channels, stacking them one above the other in frequency, and so make a composite signal representing all the channels. This operation is called frequency division. In an ideal system the bandwidth required is NB; that is, it is the sum of the bandwidths of the individual channels. Practically, we require a little more bandwidth.

Faced with the same problem of sending N channels each of bandwidth B, we can send them by time-division multiplex instead of by frequency-division multiplex. We first *completely* describe each channel by sampling the signal $2B$ times a second and by constructing a sequence of short pulses or samples which describe the amplitudes of the signal at these times. We then interleave the pulses for various channels and send them as a composite signal. The minimum bandwidth which will allow us to send these N sets of pulses, constituting $2NB$ pulses per second, is again a bandwidth $NB,$ just as in the frequency-division case.

If we introduce the same amount of noise in the common combined signal of a frequency-division or time-division system, the total noises in the received channels will be the same on both systems.

Some methods of transmission are wasteful; to send a signal of bandwidth B by amplitude modulation we must use a bandwidth $2B$. Some methods of transmission use a large bandwidth to send a signal, but gain something in doing so. High-index FM uses a large bandwidth, but the noise in the received audio signal is less than it would be if we had sent the signal by AM.

Coded signals, consisting of regularly spaced pulses which are either off or on, are particularly interesting, because they can be received and interpreted with negligible error in the presence of moderate amounts of noise. One can send the letters of the alphabet by means of such pulses, but one can also send audio signals by this means, called pulse-code modulation, or PCM. The received signal is unaffected by moderate amounts of noise introduced in transmission, but the system is not without error, for the code cannot describe with complete accuracy the amplitude to be transmitted. This error is called *quantizing noise*. Quantizing noise decreases extremely rapidly as the bandwidth used is increased so as to increase the number of pulses in each code group and hence the number of quantizing levels.

Finally, by coding it is possible actually to reduce the bandwidth needed to send a signal, but then we have to transmit a signal which is more susceptible to noise than was the original signal.

Bandwidth is important, but noise is also important. The two are in some way tied together. The exact sort of association between them, and much more besides, is the subject of *communication theory,* or *information theory,* which we will learn about in the next chapter.

CHAPTER IV

Communication Theory

As far as I can see, the terms *communication theory* and *information theory* are synonymous. I prefer the former, because it seems to me to imply less. Under one title or the other, more nonsense has been written about communication theory than about any other technical subject since the advent of relativity and quantum theory. Everyone knows meanings of the words *communication, information,* and *theory.* When people hear that there is a theory about communication they immediately want to apply it to solve their problems. The problems may lie in philosophy, in linguistics, in psychiatry, in psychology, in chemistry, or in physics. The new theory may or may not be applicable to them. Whether or no, men will speak at conferences and men will write papers. Sometimes the gist of the talk or the text is that communication theory should be applied in some field. Sometimes the claim is that it has been successfully applied. Sometimes the lofty strain is merely that communication theory is wonderful.

Here we will take a workaday view of communication theory, the view outlined at the beginning of the preceding chapter and pursued therein. A transmission system is a tool used to transmit signals from one point to another. The signals we transmit enable us to construct at some distant point a reproduction of a sound or of a scene. In order to communicate we build apparatus which transmits patterns or descriptions of things that we wish to reproduce. Some of these patterns appear to be more complicated than others. We can send roughly 1000 telephone signals over the same communication channel that can accommodate only one television signal. In this case, the distinction seems clearly to be that a television signal consists of a band of frequencies 1000 times as broad as that of a voice signal. True as this may be, it cannot completely describe the difference. We have seen in Chapter III that we can send a voice signal by high-index FM; this radio signal covers a band of frequencies much broader than the 3000 cycles used in ordinary telephony. By using this broad band, the received signal can be reconstructed with less noise. We have also seen in Chapter III that in one way at least the bandwidth needed to transmit a signal can be halved.

In the early days signals were more or less taken for granted as facts of nature. They had certain bandwidths; they required a certain fidelity of reproduction, and these requirements were to be met by rather direct means. But with the advent of broadband frequency modulation engineers were somewhat shaken. During and after World War II, several men began to speculate deeply on the nature of signals. What is it that communication systems are asked to send? How can we characterize and measure it, so that we can make valid, quantitative comparisons between diverse sorts of signals? The late Norbert Wiener's book *Cybernetics,* published in 1948, had a good deal to say about communication theory. In the same year, Claude Shannon, another mathematician, published a paper, "A Mathematical Theory of Communication," which had even more to say. Shannon's paper launched communication theory well on the way it has since taken.

Shannon found a way of characterizing signals by means of a quantity he called *amount of information.* Sometimes merely the word *information* is used as a name for this quantity. The use of *information* in this sense is taking an old word to express a very particular meaning, just as in physics *force* has a very particular meaning, completely excluding its meaning in such phrases as *force of circumstance,* or *forceful delivery,* and as in engineering *stress* has a particular narrow meaning which excludes the meanings of the word in *he was under great stress* or *great mental stress.* So, in information theory we must regard *information* as meaning no more than what we define it to mean. If we insist, for instance, that information so used must have or imply meaning, we are trying to carry into communication theory something of the useful but loose connotations of everyday language. In communication theory, *amount of information,* or more loosely, *information,* is a particular, quantitative technical term.

In communication theory, information can perhaps best be explained as choice or uncertainty. Let us consider a very simple case of communication. If you want to send a birthday greeting by telegraph, you may be offered a choice of sending one of a number of rather flowery messages, perhaps one from a list of sixteen. Thus, in this form of communication the sender has a certain definite, limited choice as to what message he will send. If you receive such a birthday telegram, there is some uncertainty as to what it will say, but not much. If it was chosen from a list of sixteen standard messages, it must be one among the sixteen. The received message must enable the recipient to decide which among the sixteen was chosen by the sender.

In order for the sender to indicate to the recipient which message he has chosen, he must use some sort of signal. One particular form of signal might be a sequence of pulses or absences of pulses, as we have discussed in Chapter III. We can think of such pulses or absences of pulses as representing a sequence of elementary choices or decisions between two alternatives. Such choices or decisions may be in various cases *pulse* or *no pulse, yes* or *no, heads* or *tails, right* or *left.* All are merely choices or decisions between alternatives, and one can be represented by any other. By means of a sequence of such elementary choices one can enlarge the number of choices. When the choices are made known to the recipient of the message, he can decide which alternative was chosen.

For instance, let us number our sixteen messages 0 to 15 and see how we can choose among them. We can follow a sort of tree of branching paths, as shown in Fig. 23. At the top are the message numbers. The sender can choose, or the recipient of the message can arrive at, any one of these by taking at

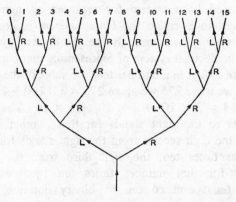

Figure 23

each branch point the *R* (right) or *L* (left) branch. To arrive at message 9, for instance, the elementary choices or decisions are *RLLR*. If we let 1 stand for *R* and 0 stand for *L*, the sequence 1001 describes the sender's choices, in order, which lead to the one message out of sixteen. For the recipient of the message, these four elementary decisions decide which message among sixteen was intended.

Thus, the number 9 can be represented by a sequence of *R*'s and *L*'s, a sequence of ones and zeros, by the code 1001. Here we have arrived at this sequence by making four *elementary choices, R* or *L*. Such elementary choices are called *bits* of information; they are the fundamental units of information by means of which any message can be specified.

The word *bit* comes from *binary digit*. While our approach to the use of 0 or 1 has been from the point of view of information theory, these digits have long been used in a system for representing numbers. This system is called the *binary system* in contrast to the system we commonly use, the *decimal system.*

In the decimal system of representing numbers, the place of a digit in a number tells the value of the digit. When we write 275 we mean $275 = 2 \times 100 + 7 \times 10 + 5 \times 1 = 2 \times 10^2 + 7 \times 10^1 + 5 \times 10^0$. The digit farthest to the right stands for that number times unity, the digit second from the right stands for that number times ten, the digit third from the right stands for that number times ten squared (ten times ten), and so on. In binary notation, 101 means

$$101 = 1 \times 4 + 0 \times 2 + 1 \times 1 =$$
$$1 \times 2^2 + 0 \times 2^1 + 1 \times 2^0 = 5$$

The digit third from the right stands for that number times two squared, and so on. Some typical binary numbers and their decimal equivalents are:

Binary	Decimal
1	1
10	2
100	4
1000	8
10,000	16
10,100	20
1001	9

Electronic computers perform their computations in the binary system. The binary system is chosen because the binary digits, 1 and 0, can be represented by a switch which is open or closed, or by a pulse which is present or absent, while the representation of a decimal digit is more complicated.

We have considered a ridiculously simple case in which the message is chosen as one among sixteen. An actual message may be a five-minute talk or a half-hour television program. How many different sequences of sounds five minutes long can you distinguish by means of the telephone? The number is fantastically large, but it is not infinite. The number of sequences of pictures which can be sent in 30 minutes by television is still larger, but it is not infinite either. Any particular message of either of these sets of messages could be described by a sufficient number of bits, of elementary pieces of information, of yeses or noes.

Communication systems provide us with channels for sending messages. Shannon has derived a fundamental law for the maximum number of bits of information which can be sent over such a channel in one second. He finds that this number of bits per second depends on the bandwidth, B, the average signal power, P_s, and the average power, P_n, of the noise which gets into the channel in one way or another. When the noise is Johnson noise or other noise having the same statistical properties, the capacity, C, of the channel for transmitting information, measured in bits per second, is

$$C = B \log_2 \left(1 + \frac{P_s}{P_n} \right) \text{ bits per second}$$

Shannon's proof says that by *sufficiently ingenious means* and by using *complicated enough equipment* we could send information over the channel up to this rate with errors occurring as infrequently as we might desire, but that if we tried to send more bits per second over the channel we would necessarily make errors; that is, the man or device receiving the message could not receive all the bits, all the yeses or noes, correctly, and so could not correctly decide exactly what message was intended by the sender.

The mathematical quantity $\log_2 (1 + P_s/P_n)$ is called the *logarithm to the base 2* of $(1 + P_s/P_n)$. It is easiest to explain the meaning of this logarithm by some examples involving $\log_2 x$:

x	log_2x
2	1
4	2
8	3

We see that

$$x = 2^{(\log_2 x)}$$

Or, the logarithm to the base 2 of the number x is the number of times 2 must be multiplied by itself to give x.

Mathematically, we can define $\log_2 x$ for values of x other than powers of 2. Some examples are given below:

x	log_2x
1	0
9	3.2
9999	13.3

Let us ask, as an example of Shannon's law, how many bits per second can be sent over a television channel if the bandwidth is 4,000,000 cycles per second and the ratio of signal power to noise power is 10,000. The answer turns out to be approximately $C = 54,000,000$ bits/second.

In Chapter III we discussed two communication systems—high-index FM and PCM—which use large bandwidth but which, to some extent, overcome noise. Shannon's law tells us what is theoretically possible along these lines. Consider the communication system indicated in Fig. 24. Here we start out

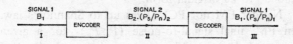

Figure 24

with some signal, 1, of bandwidth B_1; it might be a TV signal, for instance. We wish to transmit this signal from point I to some point III, and we wish it to arrive with a signal-to-noise ratio of $(P_s/P_n)_1$. However, we will transmit it over some channel, II, perhaps a microwave link, which has some other bandwidth, B_2, and some other signal-to-noise ratio $(P_s/P_n)_2$. Shannon's law says that this will be just possible if

$$B_2 \log_2 [1 + (P_s/P_n)_2] = B_1 \log_2 [1 + (P_s/P_n)_1]$$

It will certainly be possible if we make B_2 or $(P_s/P_n)_2$ greater than this relation requires.

In order to represent and transmit signal 1 by means of some other signal (which we will call signal 2), we make use of a device which we will call by the general name, *encoder*. At the far end of the transmission Channel II we make use of a *decoder* to recover the signal in its original form (plus any noise which may have been added in transmission or encoding). High-index FM and PCM, which we discussed in Chapter III, are examples of transmission in which we change the nature of the signal, or encode it, increasing its bandwidth so that even with a small transmitter power we obtain a good signal-to-noise ratio when the signal is finally "decoded" to its original form.

Neither FM nor PCM lives up to Shannon's law. In FM, final signal-to-noise $(P_s/P_n)_1$ for a given ratio $(P_s/P_n)_2$ in the transmission path II does not increase nearly as rapidly with bandwidth as it should ideally, according to Shannon. In the case of PCM, the signal-to-noise ratio $(P_s/P_n)_1$ increases in the right way with bandwidth in the Channel II, but the signal-to-noise ratio in the transmission Channel II must be around 14 times greater than the ideal. One of the chief activities of workers in the field of information theory is to seek more nearly ideal ways of encoding signals. Will this result in great changes in the way messages are transmitted in the future? Not necessarily. Although PCM is more efficient than FM, FM is often used in preference, because the apparatus needed is simpler and because FM is in some ways more adaptable to certain transmission conditions or certain signals. In the same way, PCM would be simpler than some more nearly ideal system.

In Chapter III a means of reducing the bandwidth was discussed. Is this a very practical idea? We see that if we double the bandwidth of the channel we double the channel capacity, but when we increase the transmitter power, the channel capacity increases only very slowly with an increase in the signal-to-noise ratio, P_s/P_n. This relationship is illustrated in the table below:

P_s/P_n (*signal-to-noise ratio*)	log_2 $(1 + P_s/P_n)$ (*channel capacity is proportional in this quantity*)
1	1
10	3.5
100	6.7
1000	10.0
10,000	13.3

Especially for large signal-to-noise ratios, increasing the transmitter power, P_s, increases the channel capacity only slightly. Thus, very large increases of transmitter power are required if we are to reduce the required bandwidth appreciably while sending information at a constant rate. In FM broadcast, in sending the TV sound channel, and in microwave radio relay systems one increases bandwidth in order to reduce the required power, as in high-index FM, rather than increasing the power in order to reduce the bandwidth.

However, in wire transmission circuits, such as cable pairs and coaxial cables, the loss or attenuation of a signal increases rapidly with its frequency. Thus, with a given power and over a given distance, more data (bits/second) can be sent using multilevel pulses (as discussed in Chapter III) than by using two-level or binary pulses. Thus, the trading off between bandwidth and signal-to-noise ratio is sometimes made in one direction and sometimes in another. The choice is an engineering choice, which we have to make in accordance with needs and circumstances, and what seems practical at a given time.

So far we have taken the source of the signal rather for granted, but we really should include it explicitly in the communication system. When we do, the diagram of a typical communication system is as shown in Fig. 25. At the left we have a *signal*

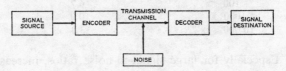

Figure 25

source, which may be a man speaking into a telephone, a scene which a television camera picks up, a girl operating a teletypewriter. We next have an *encoder,* which translates the signal into some form suitable for electrical transmission. For voice transmission this encoder might, in a particular instance, include a microphone, a device for turning the electrical signal from the microphone into PCM, and a radio transmitter for sending the PCM signal to the receiver. In transmission a certain amount of noise is added to the signal; this noise may actually be added in the radio receiver. After the signal reaches the radio receiver it is decoded by a decoder and returned to its original form. The decoder for a voice signal might include the radio receiver, a device for changing PCM into the original form of electrical signal delivered by the microphone, and a loudspeaker for changing this electrical signal into sound. Finally, as part of the over-all communication system we have the signal destination, which may be the ear of the listener or the eye of the beholder.

So far we have dealt with the capability of a channel to transmit information: the channel capacity C, which is measured in bits per second. If the channel capacity is adequate to transmit the information generated by the signal source, the actual rate of transmission must be governed by the rate at which the signal source produces information and by the rate at which the signal destination can accept information. How are we to measure these rates? We usually know the bandwidth of the signal, and we usually know the signal-to-noise ratio required at the signal destination. Can we use Shannon's formula,

$$C = B \, \log_2(1 + P_s/P_n)$$

to compute the information rate of the signal source? We cannot, and a little thought will make it clear why.

Suppose that our signal is a man talking, and we consider as a message what he may say in one second. We may wish to reproduce all the sounds of his speech which lie within a band of frequencies 3000 cycles wide, and we may wish to attain a ratio of signal power P_s (the part of the power of the reproduced sound which is an accurate reproduction of the sound of the man's voice), to noise power P_n (any other power present in the reproduced sound) of 10,000. If we use a bandwidth of 3000 cycles and a signal-to-noise ratio of 10,000, we easily calculate that the number of bits needed to describe all the distinct messages we could identify by means of a signal one second long as

$$3000 \log_2(1 + 10,000/1) = 40,000 \text{ bits}$$

Are all the messages described by this number of bits the possible messages, and only those possible messages, we might receive from a speaker? Clearly they are not, for our system would transmit and reproduce *any* sound with a bandwidth of 3000 cycles and a signal-to-noise ratio of 10,000; the roar of a lion, the babble of a brook, the sound of an orchestra, as well as the sound of a voice uttering intelligible speech. Actually, the number of spoken messages a second long is much smaller, and it could be specified by far fewer than 40,000 bits, or binary digits.

Let us now consider the signal destination, which is in this case the listener. It would be inefficient to transmit even all the sounds that a man utters in English speech, for the human ear cannot distinguish some sounds from others. For instance, Fig. 26 shows the variation of amplitude with time for two different electrical signals. Each is made up of the same frequency components, but the component sine waves of different frequencies are shifted rela-

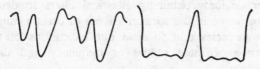

Figure 26

tive to one another in the two signals. No one can deny that these two signals are different, and yet as sound waves they would sound almost the same to the human ear.

Even before the advent of information theory, back in 1939, Homer Dudley, in order to transmit speech over a channel of very limited information rate, demonstrated a device called the vocoder, which took advantage of the limited nature of the voice to produce sounds and of the ear to distinguish sounds.

The vocoder relies on the fact that the human voice produces essentially two sorts of sounds: a buzz from the vocal cords and a hiss from the passage of air past the tongue, as in saying *s, ch, sh, th.* Accordingly, Dudley provided in the receiving part of his vocoder a source of hiss sound, a source of buzz sound, and controls for turning these on and off and for changing the pitch of the buzz sound.

These controls are not enough. As we speak, the lips and tongue modulate or filter the buzz and hiss sounds so that some frequency components are strengthened relative to others. It is this filtering action which is responsible for the distinctive sounds of the various vowels and consonants. Accordingly, Dudley provided at the transmitting end of the vocoder devices containing electrical filters to detect the presence in the speaker's voice of certain ranges of frequencies and to send out indications of the presence of these ranges of frequency and their strengths.

Thus, in sending a signal the vocoder detects whether a buzz or a hiss is present, and the pitch of the buzz if a buzz is present. It also detects what bands of frequencies of the buzz or hiss are emphasized and how strongly they are emphasized. It sends this information to the reproducing part of the vocoder, where a hiss or a buzz of appropriate pitch is generated, and the appropriate ranges of frequencies are emphasized in appropriate degrees. The result is an intelligible re-creation of the original speech!

The re-created speech is not a result of transmitting and reproducing the exact variations with time of the electrical signal from the microphone which picks up the speech. In fact, the wave form of the re-created speech may bear little resemblance to that of the speech to be transmitted. But the re-created speech *sounds* like the original speech, not exactly so, but recognizably so. And it can be transmitted, using a total bandwidth of less than 1000 cycles instead of 3000 cycles. Apparently, the information rate of speech is not more than a third the information rate of a channel which will transmit not only speech but any other sound as well!

Most signal sources can generate in each second far fewer distinct messages than we might at first think. The vocoder demonstrates this in the case of speech. It is true also for television. In television, for instance, thirty distinct pictures are transmitted each second. The television transmitter and channel could send an entirely different picture each time, yet, by and large, successive pictures are much the same. The actual information needed to tell what the next picture will be is less than the system is capable of transmitting, and so the system is in this respect inefficient. Likewise, as the electron beam of the pickup tube scans from one picture element to the next, the change of brightness is likely to be small, and on the average not much information is needed to specify the difference in brightness between one picture element and the next. Yet the television system is capable of transmitting a picture in which each picture element is wildly different from the one preceding it. This capability is never called on in transmitting actual pictures, and so the television system is inefficient in providing more capabilities, more channel capacity, than is needed to transmit actual pictures.

We have a measure of the capacity of a channel to transmit information; this is the channel capacity C, measured in bits per second. It is easily calculated in terms of the bandwidth and signal-to-noise ratio of the channel. With actual signals, such as FM and PCM, we fall short of transmitting this much information.

A signal source also has a number of bits per second attached to it; this is the *average* rate at which the signal source generates information. This rate, which is also measured in bits per second, is the information rate of the signal source. It is also called the *entropy rate* of the signal source. It is a measure of the amount of freedom or choice the signal source has in generating a message a second long. It is a measure of the amount of uncertainty the signal destination has in determining which, among many messages one second long, a particular message may be. Usually, the information or entropy rate of a signal source is much smaller than one might at first think. It is difficult to evaluate it, for signals are very complicated.

Once we know enough about a signal to evaluate its information rate, we ought to be able to encode the signal for transmission so that we could send it over a channel with a channel capacity C no greater than the information rate of the source. Sometimes, as in the case of the vocoder, we can go a long way in this direction. Usually, however, the process is complicated and the results may be far from perfect.

Usually, in fact, it is cheaper to encode the signal by some very simple means and to use a great excess of channel capacity to transmit it rather than to provide the complicated encoding and decoding apparatus needed to send the signal with reduced channel capacity. That is the chief reason why devices such as vocoders are not actually used in telephony. Bandwidth is cheaper than vocoders. However, vocoders are used in the transmission of encrypted speech.

Communication theory has given us a broad and important insight into the over-all problem of encoding messages for transmission over communication channels, but it has in general not provided us with particular, practical new ways for transmitting voice or television signals. Communication theory has had, however, an increasing impact on the transmission of data signals from computers and other sources. Here the problem is not that of evaluating the entropy of the signal source, which is usually assumed to be one bit per binary pulse. Rather, the problem is that of transmitting sequences of binary digits without error over a noisy channel which, as we have noted in Chapter III, may sometimes change a 0 into a 1 or a 1 into a 0. To this end, information theorists have worked out many varieties of error-correcting codes. Examples of error correcting codes devised by R. W. Hamming were mentioned by Shannon in his original paper. Later, Marcel J. E. Golay published concerning error-correcting codes in 1949, and Hamming published his work in 1950. We should note that these codes were devised subsequent to Shannon's work. They *might,* I suppose, have been devised before, but it was only when Shannon showed error-free transmission to be possible that people asked, "How can we achieve it?"

We cannot examine these in detail or discuss their advantages and disadvantages, but we can consider a simple and primitive example which shows that such error correction is possible. One way of getting error correction is to encode a long block of message digits at a time. As a simple example, suppose we encode our message digits in blocks of 16 and add after each block a sequence of *check digits* which enable us to detect a single error in *any one* of the digits, message digits or check digits. As a particular example, consider the sequence of message digits 1 1 0 1 0 0 1 1 0 1 0 1 1 0 0 0. To find the appropriate check digits, we write the

0's and 1's constituting the message digits in the 4-by-4 grid shown in Fig. 27. Associated with each

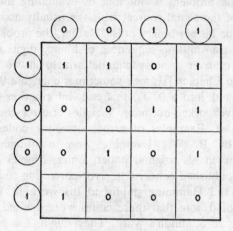

Figure 27

row and each column is a circle. Each circle contains a 0 or a 1, whichever is needed to make the total number of 1's in the column or row (including the circle as well as the squares) even. These added digits are check digits. For the particular assortment of message digits used as an example, together with the appropriately chosen check digits, the numbers of ones in successive columns (left to right) are 2, 2, 2, 4, all being even numbers, and the numbers of 1's in successive rows (top to bottom) are 4, 2, 2, 2, which are again all even.

What happens if a single error is made in the transmission of a message digit among the 16? There will be an odd number of ones *in a row and in a column.* This tells us to change the message digit where the row and column intersect. And if a single error is made in a check digit? There will be an odd number of ones *in a row or in a column.* We have detected an error, but we see that it was not among the message digits.

The total number of digits transmitted for 16 message digits is $16 + 8$, or 24; we have increased the number of digits needed in the ratio 24/16, or 1.5. If we had started out with 400 message digits, we would have needed 40 check digits and we would have increased the number of digits needed only in the ratio of 440/400, or 1.1. Of course, we would have been able to correct only one error in 440 rather than one error in 24.

Codes can be devised which can be used to correct larger numbers of errors in a block of transmitted characters. Of course, more check digits are needed to correct more errors.

CHAPTER V

Communication through Space

When physics students use James Clerk Maxwell's equations to study the behavior of electromagnetic waves, they first study waves in empty space, the simplest waves of all. Advanced students may later try to cope with wave propagation in the atmosphere, whose variations in temperature and density make radio waves shimmer, even as the light from objects shimmers when we view them through the hot and disturbed air above a fire. They will study the bending of extremely short radio waves by layers in the atmosphere; this bending can cause radio waves to arrive at the receiver over two or more paths of different lengths. They may study the propagation of radio waves through the charged layers of the ionosphere, which bend radio waves of frequencies from 10 to 30 megacycles back toward earth (or we would not be able to receive them thousands of miles away). Or, advanced students may study the propagation of light waves through sequences of lenses, or of very short, high-frequency radio waves through carefully made but nonetheless imperfect metal tubes called waveguides.

From the invention of radio to the coming of the space age, radio engineers had to contend, not with simple textbook problems, but with complicated, messy, intractable problems. Technology provided increasingly powerful resources, but nature remained obdurate. The radio waves traveled not through emptiness, but through the earth's atmosphere. If only, some of us lamented, we had the easy task of communicating through empty space rather than the difficult task of communicating through the troubled air! As I wrote in 1952, "The difficulty will be in getting to the stars, not in telegraphing home about it." Arthur C. Clarke had pointed out earlier, in 1945, the potentialities of satellites for communication between pairs of earth stations—once satellites could be launched into orbit.

With the launching of Sputnik I in 1957, communication engineers at last could use that simple, ideal medium which had hitherto been available only in textbooks. At low radio frequencies the ionosphere bars radio waves from space. As the frequency is increased above 10,000 megacycles, the earth's atmosphere gradually becomes opaque to radio waves. But, over a range of thousands of megacycles, waves pass readily out of the earth's atmosphere. Going straight up, the total mass of air we encounter is less than the equivalent of seven miles of air at sea level density. And, instead of passing glancingly along layers in the atmosphere as radio waves do in earth-bound radio systems, radio waves directed upward pass quickly through such layers and are little affected by them.

The story of what communication engineers have done with the fascinating possibilities of space is an engaging one, and it is particularly appropriate because the communication problems are so much simpler than those encountered in earthbound systems. The difficulties lie outside the field of communication, in launching, guiding, and controlling the attitude of space vehicles. The challenge here is indeed real and difficult. Without boosters and astrogation, we could no more have communication through space than we could have submarine cables across the oceans without ships to lay them and navigators to guide the ships.

The communication equipment in space must of course operate with great reliability unattended and in a strange environment. But this is the sort of problem which communication engineers had long coped with. It is certainly no more difficult than problems of the unattended amplifiers or *repeaters* of submarine telephone cables, which must work perfectly for years at the bottom of the ocean. The communication art was ripe for the exploitation of space when Sputnik was launched.

It would take a great many words to discuss all the interesting space communication experiments and applications, so I propose to select a few simple and instructive ones.

Though I will not discuss it in detail, it is important to note that the Army's Score satellite launched on December 18, 1958, was both the first communication satellite and the first *active* communication satellite; that is, the first to carry a radio receiver and transmitter. Score relayed messages between ground stations in Arizona, Georgia, and Texas, and transmitted a recorded Christmas message by President Eisenhower. Batteries which ultimately ran down powered Score, and voice signals terminated on December 31, after thirteen days of operation.

In the early days of satellite communication many people, myself included, were worried about hurrying into the launching of electronic equipment. We knew that this could and would be done, but we also knew how many years' work go into the development of highly reliable equipment, such as submarine cable repeaters, and we worried lest the hurried launching of complicated electronic equipment should result in failure. There was an alternative which I had pointed out in 1954. That was to launch, not a radio receiver and transmitter, but a huge ball or balloon which would reflect back to an earth-based receiver part of the energy beamed at it from an earth-based transmitter.

In January 1956, William J. O'Sullivan of the Langley Research Laboratory of the National Advisory Committee for Aeronautics (now incorporated in the National Aeronautics and Space Administration) had proposed to launch balloon satellites in order to measure atmospheric density at an altitude of around 1000 miles. His work led to the construction of an experimental 100-foot aluminized plastic balloon. In 1958 a colleague, Rudolf Kompfner, and I saw in O'Sullivan's balloon the very object I had thought of as a communication satellite in 1954. William H. Pickering, the head of the Jet Propulsion Laboratory, agreed that an experiment with O'Sullivan's balloon would be a profitable one, and offered his encouragement and support.

This undertaking led to Echo I, which NASA launched on August 12, 1960. On its first orbit this

satellite carried a spoken message by President
Eisenhower from the Jet Propulsion Laboratory's
earth station at Goldstone, California, to an earth
station that the Bell Telephone Laboratories had
built at Crawford Hill, New Jersey.

I will not dwell on the remarkable feat of launching and inflating the Echo balloon, nor the remarkable feat of finding and tracking it automatically by
means of computed orbital data. Rather, we will discuss the communication aspects of Echo I. Particularly, let us consider how much of the transmitted
power reached the receiver.

There is a simple transmission formula relating
the power P_R received by a microwave antenna to
the power P_T transmitted by another microwave
antenna, when they are pointed at one another. It is

$$\frac{P_R}{P_T} = \frac{A_R A_T}{\lambda^2 L^2}$$

Here λ is the wavelength and L is the separation of
the antennas. A_R is the *effective area* of the receiving antenna and A_T is the effective area of the transmitting antenna. Microwave antennas are usually
huge parabolic *dishes* or reflectors. For such an-
tennas the effective area is from $\frac{1}{2}$ to $\frac{3}{4}$ of the area of
the reflector, seen looking directly at it.

The transmitting antenna at Goldstone was an 85-
foot parabolic reflector, with an effective area of
around 2900 square feet. The 100-foot Echo balloon itself had a cross-sectional area of 7850 square
feet. The wavelength was .4 foot (corresponding to
a frequency of 2390 mc). The altitude of Echo I
was about 1000 miles; we will assume that the slant

range from the transmitter (and from the receiver) to be 1500 miles or 8×10^6 feet. From the equation, the fraction of the transmitter power which struck Echo was

$$\frac{P_R}{P_T} = \frac{(2900)(7850)}{(.4)^2(8 \times 10^6)^2} = 2.2 \times 10^{-6}$$

The radio waves which strike a large sphere are scattered nearly equally in all directions, over a solid angle of 4π steradians. The receiving antenna covers a solid angle of A_R/L^2 steradians. Hence, of the power reflected by the balloon, the fraction which is received by the receiving antenna on earth is $A_R/4\pi L^2$. The receiving antenna at Crawford Hill had an effective area of 280 square feet. Using this and the distance of 8×10^6 feet, we find that the fraction of the power scattered from Echo I which reached the receiving antenna to be

$$\frac{280}{4\pi(8 \times 10^6)^2} = 3.5 \times 10^{-13}$$

Thus, the fraction of the transmitter power that reached the receiver was

$$(2.2 \times 10^{-6})(3.5 \times 10^{-13}) = 7.7 \times 10^{-19}$$

About a *billionth of a billionth* of the power transmitted from Goldstone reached the receiver at Crawford Hill. Expressed in db, the receiver power was -181 db with respect to the transmitter power. The transmitter power was 10,000 watts or 40 dbw. Hence, the receiver power was 7.7×10^{-15} watts, or -141 dbw.

It would have been impossible to achieve satisfactory voice communication had an ordinary micro-wave receiver been used. But quantum electronics had provided communication technology with an ex-tremely low noise receiver, with a noise power cor-responding to that emitted by an object held at only 25° Kelvin, or 248° below zero Centigrade. This re-ceiver was only about a hundredth as noisy as the "good" conventional microwave receivers of that time. For a 3000-cycle bandwidth and a noise tem-perature of 25°K the equivalent noise power at the input of the receiver was 10^{-18} watt. Hence, the ratio of signal power to noise power was about 7700. The signal-to-noise ratio was considerably less than this when the satellite was near the horizon, both because the satellite was then farther away and because the receiving antenna picked up more John-son noise from the warm and imperfectly transpar-ent (to microwaves) atmosphere in looking through it at a grazing angle.

Several forms of modulation were used in the Echo I experiment, including merely shifting the voice signal up in frequency to the microwave range (called *single sideband*—this is the same process as used in frequency-division multiplex). Wide devia-tion frequency modulation was also used. A consid-erable improvement in the signal-to-noise ratio of the voice signal was obtained.

Echo I was used to relay voice, facsimile, and data signals from one ground location to another. It was invaluable in showing that extremely low noise re-ceiving systems could be built and used, and that antennas could be made to track satellites automati-cally by means of computed orbital data. But Echo I was an experiment, not a prototype of satellite for a commercial communication system. Echo I was an extremely expensive way of providing a single telephone channel across a continent or an ocean.

On October 4, 1960, Courier 1-B was launched under Army cognizance. This complicated active communication satellite failed after seventeen days. Perhaps there had been an effort to do too much too soon.

Echo had stirred up tremendous enthusiasm, which inspired the American Telephone & Telegraph Company to undertake the construction of an active communication satellite and a huge ground terminal at a cost of around $50 million. NASA agreed to supply AT&T with boosters; the price was $3.5 million per launch, a worldwide license under all inventions in the satellite field, and a right to license anyone else under these inventions. The British and French, at their own expense, built earth stations suitable for use with the Telstar communications satellite.

The Telstar I satellite was launched for AT&T by NASA on July 10, 1962. It was a technical and popular success. A United States Information Agency poll showed that in the weeks after the transatlantic television ceremonies (which were carried between Europe and the United States on July 23, 1962) 82 per cent of the people of Great Britain were able to identify the Telstar satellite by name, 79 per cent knew that it was an American achievement, and 59 per cent saw the television program beamed from the United States.

The Telstar satellite could be used to transmit

television, or 600 one-way telephone channels, or 12 two-way telephone channels across the ocean because it supplied more power to the receiver than Echo did, and the ground station had a larger antenna than that of the Echo experiment and so picked up a larger fraction of the power directed at the earth. The Telstar satellite sent out radio waves almost equally in all directions. The earth terminal at Andover, Maine has an effective area of about 2500 square feet. When the Telstar satellite was 5000 miles or 2.5×10^7 feet away, the fraction of the power from the Telstar satellite which was picked up by the Andover antenna was

$$\frac{2500}{4 \ (2.6 \times 10^7)^2} = 2.9 \times 10^{-13}$$

The traveling-wave tube aboard the Telstar satellite had a power of about 2 watts, so the power received by the Andover antenna was about

$$5.8 \times 10^{-13} \text{ watts}$$

This is about seventy-five times the power received from Echo I, even though the distance is greater (5000 miles vs. 1500 miles) and the power transmitted by the Telstar satellite was only 2 watts. It is this larger received power that made it possible for the Telstar satellite to transmit television pictures or many telephone messages. The greater height meant that the Telstar satellite could be seen from both sides of the Atlantic for considerable periods.

The Telstar I satellite finally became inoperative because of radiation in space, which was much higher than expected. The Telstar II satellite, launched on

May 7, 1963, was made satisfactorily radiation resistant. Satellites of the Telstar type could have formed the basis of a commercial communication system.

NASA's Relay I satellite, built by RCA and launched on December 14, 1962, was somewhat similar to the Telstar satellite. Relay was a worthy experiment, but we learned little from it that we did not know from the Telstar satellite. Syncom is a different story.

Syncom is the outcome of the bold and ingenious belief of a group of engineers at Hughes that one could make an extremely small but reliable synchronous satellite and successfully launch it with the rather small Thor-Delta vehicle used to launch such low-altitude satellites as Echo, Telstar, and Relay. Attitude control was maintained merely by spinning, with a jet system for corrections of axis and position. No battery was incorporated; the satellite operated only when in sunlight. Everything was cut to the bone. But, though the first launch on February 14, 1963 failed, Syncom II, launched on July 26, 1963, and Syncom III, launched on August 19, 1964, succeeded, and have operated well ever since.

While radio transmission via satellite is much simpler than radio transmission in terrestrial systems, the time it takes a radio wave to travel to and from a satellite leads to some difficulty in conversing via satellite.

Long-distance or trunk telephone circuits use separate paths in the two directions; the circuits from switching offices to subscribers send signals both ways over the same pair of wires. Devices called hybrid coils are used to attain some degree of independence of transmission in the two directions. Nonetheless, all the world's 180 million telephones reflect a small percentage of energy directed toward them. When the person on the phone hears this reflected speech delayed by 0.1 second or more, he finds it unpleasant and upsetting. Thus, echo suppressors are inserted at the ends of trunk circuits longer than 1500 miles. These devices turn off the outward path when a signal is present on the inward path. Provision is made for breaking in by talking very loudly.

Echo suppressors are tolerable for handling echoes with the delays encountered in continental telephony and even in transoceanic telephony by way of submarine cable. Are they tolerable for an echo delayed 0.6 second, as would be the case in talking by way of a synchronous satellite? This is no easy matter to decide, for the answer could depend on the people involved, on the nature of the conversation, and perhaps on the design of the echo suppressor. Psychologists have been studying this problem at the Bell Laboratories for over four years. As in most experiments, answering one question raises another.

Tests are still going on. The conclusion seems to be firmer and firmer that a fraction of users will find any two-wire circuit with any existing echo suppressor somewhat unsatisfactory when the round trip delay is as long as that in a synchronous satellite circuit. All echo suppressors interrupt the two-way connection, and that is what does the damage. In the future it may become possible to cancel out echoes by means of an adaptive network. But at least until or unless this can be done commercially, synchronous satellite circuits will remain usable but noticeably inferior to cable circuits for telephony.

On August 31, 1962, the Communications Satellite Act became law, establishing the Communications Satellite Corporation, or Comsat, as the sole American agency for launching and owning satellites for communication with foreign countries. Progress has been slow but steady. At the writing of this book, Comsat is using Early Bird, an improved version of Syncom, to provide commercial transatlantic telephone and television service. Comsat plans to launch several synchronous satellites to give NASA communication between various earth sites as a part of the Apollo man-to-the-moon program. Comsat also plans to launch improved satellites for common carrier transoceanic telephone and television transmission.

What are the prospects of communications satellites? It appears that they may be economical for domestic as well as international communication. ABC asked the Federal Communications Commission for permission to establish a communications satellite system for television network use, to link various cities together. The Ford Foundation proposed a special system for television networks. The American Telephone & Telegraph Company and Western Union have both asked Comsat to discuss the establishment of a satellite system for domestic communication. It appears that today's communication technology and today's boosters could be used to launch one synchronous satellite which could provide around 100,000 telephone circuits between various cities of the United States.

At the very beginning of this book I pointed out that electrical communication is adapted to the needs, desires, and capacities of man—his need to communicate at a distance, his desire to hear a voice or see a distant scene, and his capacity for hearing and seeing. We all have such needs and desires, and the telegraph, the telephone, television, and radio satisfy them in our everyday lives. But the aspirations of man go beyond his immediate needs. Through the ages men have built palaces, pyramids, and cathedrals as well as houses, schools, and hospitals. Utilitarian structures grow from man's desire to improve his physical and intellectual condition. Non-utilitarian architectural marvels are inherently different. They reflect man's desire to go beyond his everyday life, to reach out. Over all history, nations have spent part of their substance on monuments, pageants, and adventures.

Space is a great adventure of our age, a monument to our technical prowess. In our space program the prodigious technical resources and vast wealth of our nation have been extended and spent in a monumental effort which has been established as a national goal. The chief and most costly part of this program is Apollo—landing men on the moon and returning them safely to earth. Mercury and Gemini have been amazingly successful steps in this direction. But to me, the most exciting feat has been one which has nothing to do with the Apollo program. That has been the transmission of photographs of Mars to the earth by Mariner IV. One day there was uncertainty and argument as to the nature of Mars. Were there really canals? What was the surface like? The next day man's sight had been extended over 150 million miles, and we knew Mars to be a scarred and cratered planet, resembling the moon more than the romantic planet of science fiction. The advance over telescopic observation of the planet is prodigious.

Mars is never closer to the earth than 35 million miles, and after flying past Mars, Mariner IV had to be capable of transmitting pictures back from a distance of up to 160 million miles or 8.5×10^{11} feet. This challenge in communication is worthy of discussion and description.

Mariner carried equipment which tracked the star Canopus and the sun; this orientation made it possible to point a high-gain microwave antenna, with a beamwidth of between 10 and 20 degrees, at an 85-foot diameter tracking antenna on earth. The effective area of the antenna aboard Mariner was 3.0 square feet. The effective area of the earth antenna was 2300 square feet. The frequency of transmission from Mariner to earth was 2298 megacycles, corresponding to a wavelength of 0.42 foot.

According to the equation given earlier in this chapter, the ratio of received power P_R to transmitted power P_T was

$$\frac{P_R}{P_T} = \frac{(3.0)(2300)}{(.42)^2(8.5 \times 10^{11})^2} = 5.4 \times 10^{-20}$$

This can be expressed as −193 db. The power transmitted by Mariner was 38 dbw (about 6 watts), so the received signal was about −185 dbw. The sensitive receiver at the earth station operated with a noise temperature of 45°K. The effective bandwidth used in transmission was only about 12 cycles. The Johnson noise corresponding to a temperature of 45°K and a bandwidth of 12 cycles is

$$7.45 \times 10^{-21} \text{ watt or } -209 \text{ dbw}$$

Thus, the signal power was about 24 db (250 times) greater than the noise power in a 12-cycle band. This power is more than sufficient for receiving binary digits, which were transmitted at a rate of $8\frac{1}{3}$ per second. The signal power in fact allows an ample *margin* against less-than-perfect performance—slight mispointing of the antennas, for instance.

Each picture transmitted by Mariner nominally had 200-by-200 picture elements in each direction, or 40,000 in all. Some of these were used for synchronization, so that only 195 by 170 or 33,150 contributed to the actual picture. In the twenty-one pictures plus 22 lines transmitted, there was a total of 699,890 picture elements.

Each of the 33,150 elements of a picture was encoded by six times this number, or 198,900 binary digits. These were transmitted at a rate of $8\frac{1}{3}$ a second, so the total transmission time for all the binary digits representing the picture was 23,868 seconds, or about 6.6 hours. Actually, on the average, it took over $8\frac{1}{2}$ hours to transmit each picture. The total time for sending the twenty-one pictures was over nine days.

In order that the pictures could be transmitted back at this leisurely rate, the binary digits representing each picture were recorded on a continuous loop of magnetic tape capable of storing 5,240,000 binary digits. The recording was done at a rate of

10,700 binary digits a second, compared with the playback and transmission rate of $8\frac{1}{3}$ binary digits a second.

Mariner IV and its mission are triumphs of technology. Taking the pictures of Mars and transmitting them back to the earth composed a very small part of the technical challenge, but achieving this with equipment which had been in space for eight months was a worthy feat.

Though the preceding chapter was devoted to communication theory, communication theory has not been mentioned in this one. It seems to me to be interesting to ask what part, if any, communication theory played in the Mariner communication problem.

Let us consider first the information rate of the source. We have noted that in television one frame is much like the preceding one, and because this similarity reduces the uncertainty as to what the next picture will be, it reduces the information rate, in bits per frame. But all the Mariner pictures are different. We have noted also that for the scenes with which we are familiar, adjacent picture elements have similar brightness. Again, this similarity reduces the uncertainty as to what the brightness of the next picture element will be, and hence, the information rate in bits per picture element. But it would have been very daring indeed to have guessed in advance what a picture of Mars might be like, and then to have designed an encoding system to transmit that type of picture only. The designers of Mariner were wise to allot six binary digits to the transmission of the brightness of each picture element.

By their foresight, the picture could be transmitted even if it was as speckled as the "snow" in a noisy TV picture.

Thus, information theory was not invoked in seeking to encode the pictures to be transmitted into a smaller number of binary digits. Was information theory used in choosing an optimum signal for transmitting binary digits over the radio channel? Let us apply Shannon's formula for channel capacity C to the Mariner radio channel. The formula is

$$C = B \log_2 (1 + P_s/P_n) \text{ bits/second}$$

We have noted that for a bandwidth of 12 cycles the ratio of signal power to noise power is 250 times. The corresponding information rate is

230 bits/second

The bandwidth is, of course, rather arbitrary. If we made the bandwidth very large, the noise power, which is proportional to bandwidth, would increase and the signal-to-noise ratio would decrease. Nonetheless, the channel capacity as given by Shannon's formula would increase, and for large bandwidths it would approach

3000 bits/second

The actual bit rate of $8\frac{1}{3}$ bits/second is only 1/22 of 230 bits/second and 1/360 of 3000 bits/second. Why is the actual bit rate so much less than that ideally attainable? Partly, because the signal-to-noise ratio was made deliberately higher than the minimum necessary in order to guard against malfunction; partly, because we do not know how to approach the ideal channel capacity very closely; partly, because it would have been unwise to put very complicated encoding equipment, which might fail, aboard the Mariner spacecraft. I have spared the reader a description of the system of modulation or encoding used in the Mariner spacecraft. I will say only that it was simple, ingenious, reliable, and well suited to the purpose.

Workers at MIT's Lincoln Laboratory have devised a complex and ingenious coding scheme using error correction for communicating simultaneously from many earth stations through military communication satellites. This system increases severalfold the number of messages which can be transmitted via one satellite. It represents an ingenious application of ideas which have grown out of Shannon's communication theory. Workers at the Bell Telephone Laboratories have used error-correcting codes and multilevel quantized transmission to increase by severalfold the number of bits per second which can be transmitted over existing telephone circuits—another ingenious application of ideas which have evolved from information theory.

Whether simple or elaborate encoding will be used depends on many aspects of a communication job. In space projects, for instance, cost doesn't count as much as it does, for example, in telephony. Costly as the Mariner mission was, its cost per citizen is small compared with his general living expenses, and the cost is hidden away in the taxes he pays. It would matter a lot to you and me if our telephone bill or the cost of our car or our food were doubled. It wouldn't be critical to the nation if the cost of the space program were doubled, any more than Cheops would have been daunted had his great pyramid taken longer to build. Of course, NASA tries not to waste money, but the primary criteria of the space program are speed and success—in a word, reliability. Another chief characteristic is that only a few of each item are made; space is no field for the sort of mass production that is characteristic of telephones or cars, or most consumer and capital goods.

The need for reliability in telephonic and other utilitarian communication is just as great as the need for reliability in space. Indeed, submarine telephone repeaters must function unattended for tens of years. But cost is also vital. Cost can be reduced by careful, painstaking research and design, which often extend over many years, and by mass production on the largest scale feasible.

Complex techniques which grow out of communication theory will be used in the space program if they make possible something that would otherwise be impossible, or if they increase the probability of the success of a mission. Such techniques will be used in common carrier communication if they decrease cost without compromising reliability.

CHAPTER VI

The Real Challenge

Last summer I had lunch with a charming French couple who had spent a year in this country and were about to return home. I asked them if any particular aspects of our life had surprised them. They told me two things. Life, recreation, how one spends one's time are less planned, less formal, more on the spur of the moment here than in France. And, if in France one wishes to make a long-distance telephone call, one first makes sure of a free afternoon in which to put it through. One can't simply lift the receiver and dial a distant city. I think that these two observations may be related. If one can telephone freely one needn't plan so far ahead or so elaborately.

This book continually reminds the reader that electrical communication serves man, and its technological resources must be matched to human senses and to human needs. To attain this match, we have to understand both technological resources and human nature.

Thus, in the last chapter we examined some of the technological marvels of communication by means of electromagnetic waves—the marvels of communication through space. In another book of this series,

Quantum Electronics, I discussed the possibilities opened up by *lasers,* which generate coherent light, and in still another book, *Electrons and Waves,* the opportunities afforded by very short radio waves, whose wavelength is only a few millimeters. Earlier in this book we considered some devices which are essential to communication—telephone transmitters and receivers, television pickup tubes, and television picture tubes. Computer input and output devices are also important to human communication.

The idea of sending 200 television signals or 100,000 telephone conversations through one two-inch tube or *waveguide* by means of radio waves a few millimeters long is glamorous. So is the idea of sending thousands or millions of messages by means of lasers and coherent light. A few years ago, coaxial cables and microwave radio systems were just as glamorous. But the problem of communication is to take advantage of these resources, to organize them into a communication system. All these means of transmission are merely alternatives to other ways of sending large bundles of messages—telephone, television, and data—between the cities of our nation. Neither satellites, nor submarine cables, nor coaxial cables, nor microwave radio systems, nor waveguides, nor lasers can connect a person in one home or office with a person in another home or office. And another new marvel, electronic switching, which is related to the electronic computer, can in the main be merely a better or cheaper or somewhat more effective means for doing things that are already being done or can be done by electromechanical switching systems.

The impact of electrical communication on our lives, and what impact it will have in the future, can be strengthened by particular technological advances. But the nature and impact of electrical communication cannot be understood by discussing such advances in detail. Electrical communication is a large, widespread, integrated system of devices and technologies. These serve needs which have come into being since Alexander Graham Bell invented the telephone. And in the future, electrical communication will certainly bring new needs into being. It is a mistake to think that science and technology merely fill needs. Quite as much, they create needs. The needs for the telephone and the automobile grew out of the uses that have been made of these devices. Communication, together with transportation and other aspects of our technology, not only creates new needs which it can satisfy and extend but shapes the whole pattern of our civilization and society. To see this, we have only to cast our minds back to times that we of middle age can remember, and then to think of the world about us.

When I was a boy in St. Paul, Minnesota, fifty years ago, we did not have a car. We lived on or near a streetcar line. When we wanted to buy things other than groceries and meat, we took the streetcar to the center of town. When we went to a lake for a vacation in the summer, we lived in a cottage near the interurban trolley. Ours was a confined life compared with that of today. We went as far as the streetcars or the trains took us in narrow patterns around the city and over the country.

The automobile, together with the telephone and

electric power, has made it possible for people to live remote from public transportation and remote from their places of work. Along with bottled gas and septic tanks, cars, telephones, and electricity have enabled people of modest means to live at a high level of contemporary comfort far even from standardized suburbs or small communities. Yet, through radio and television as means of mass communication, and through telephone and automobile as individual means of communication, men separated in space can keep in as close touch with current events as they care to. The system of marketing has followed the population away from the centers of the cities, so that there is no real need for man to travel to and from a few central points.

The first characteristic of successful communication in such a society must be a universality of communication. Communication must interconnect everyone, everywhere. Further, it must do this without let or hindrance.

When I was a boy in St. Paul, there were two competing and noninterconnecting telephone companies. One either had one phone and reached a single set of subscribers, or one had to have two phones to reach all subscribers. Happily, today nearly all phones in any country—in fact, nearly all phones in the world—interconnect. Without such universality, telephones would be of limited use. But by universality I mean more than interconnection of telephones. It seems to me that one should be able to obtain from one source all the sorts of electrical communication, to intermingle or single out on demand. One shouldn't have to patch together a communication service from elements purveyed by various suppliers. Universality need not mean common ownership of all facilities. When I call someone in London, I use facilities owned by various agencies. But I deal with one company, whether it is a Bell System telephone company or a non-Bell company. I don't have to arrange for the call with all the owners of the equipment I use. It seems to me that electrical communication without universality must be limited and cumbersome.

How can this universality be attained in practice? Let us consider telephony as an example. Although most of the world's 182 million telephones interconnect, we will consider only the 95 million telephones in North America. Among 95 million telephones there are over 4×10^{15} possible interconnections. It is ridiculous even to imagine a number like this of individual circuits interconnecting the telephones of the country. Clearly, some more sensible means of interconnection must be used. Fig. 28 gives a clue. The "subscriber loop" from your house goes to a *local central office,* along with a few hundred to as many as 50,000 other subscriber loops. When you talk to another subscriber who is connected to the same central office, your loop is connected to his loop right at that office. In a large metropolitan area there will be many central offices. When there is a great volume of traffic between nearby offices, these offices will be interconnected by *interoffice trunks.* Thus, when you talk to a subscriber whose loop is connected to a central office other than your own, your call may travel between the offices over an interoffice trunk.

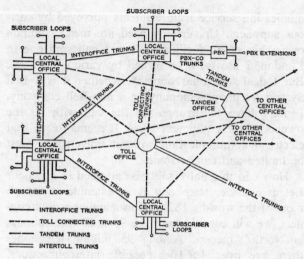

Figure 28

For a large number of central offices in one area it is uneconomical to provide an adequate number of trunks, just as it is uneconomical to interconnect all telephones pair by pair. Instead, a *tandem office* is used, connected to each of the local central offices it serves by *tandem trunks*. So, in talking to a subscriber whose loop is connected to a central office other than your own, your call *may* go from your central office to a tandem office, and from that tandem office to the other central office involved. Finally, you may wish to talk to someone in a distant city. Your call will go from your local central office to a toll office, and thence over a toll connecting trunk to some other toll office or central office.

There are many *toll circuits* interconnecting toll

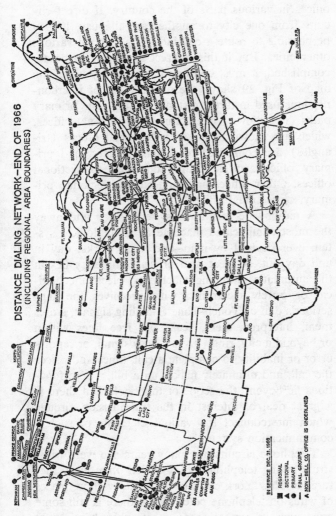

DISTANCE DIALING NETWORK—END OF 1966
(INCLUDING REGIONAL AREA BOUNDARIES)

IN SERVICE DEC. 31, 1966

■ REGIONAL
▲ SECTIONAL
● PRIMARY
● FINAL GROUPS
▲ NON-BELL CO. OFFICE IS UNDERLINED

Figure 29

offices in various parts of the country. If direct circuits from one city to another are all busy, it may be possible to route a call indirectly through various other cities. But if this indirect routing is to be accomplished, it must be done in an orderly way. The map of Fig. 29 shows the organization of interconnections used in direct distance dialing. The primary paths (not shown) interconnect the regional offices, which are shown as squares. Sectional offices (triangles) are connected to regional offices, and primary offices (circles) are connected to sectional offices. Other offices are connected to regional, primary, or sectional offices.

A nationwide telephone system is far and away the most complicated machine or technological system ever devised by man—and it all works, day in and day out. A great deal of the complexity lies in the automatic switching machinery, electromechanical or purely electronic, which receives the subscriber's dial or Touch-Tone ® dialing signals, stores them, interprets them, seeks out free lines within or beyond a city, rings, gives a busy signal, or reports error or inability to complete a call, times and prices the call, and ultimately makes up a bill. These functions lie beyond the scope of this book. But there is a great deal of interest in the transmission circuits which interconnect the various elements of such a communication system.

Telephone circuits not many years ago were wires strung along telephone poles—called *open wire*. Pictures of New York early in this century show mazes of wires on telephone poles. While there is still some open wire in remote areas, most subscribers' loops are pairs of wires twisted together, and bound with many other twisted pairs in a cable covered with lead or with layers of plastic and aluminum foil. Such cables may be hung from poles or buried in protective conduits underground. In cities most subscribers' loops are less than a mile long. In suburban areas they may be a few miles long, and in rural areas, ten or more miles long.

The power loss in a subscriber's loop can vary over a considerable range. Automatic circuits in the subscriber's telephone set compensate for a fair range of loss. When subscribers' loops are short, fine wires can be used. When they are several miles long, coarser wires can be used, or a simple transistor *voice frequency repeater* can be used to amplify the signal. Similar considerations apply to interoffice trunks. Here the maximum allowed loss depends on whether the trunk is between two central offices, or between a central office and a toll office. Long trunks can be made of larger wire than short trunks, or they can be equipped with voice frequency amplifiers.

But there is an alternative in providing circuits between offices. If the distance is great enough, it is cheaper to send many messages over two pairs of wires (one pair for each direction—this is called *four-wire* transmission) by means of time division multiplex or frequency division multiplex than it is to provide a separate pair of wires for each circuit. In such short-haul multiplex systems there is a considerable cost for the terminals which convert from voice frequency to a higher frequency and back, and an additional cost incurred in transforming dial

113

pulses and other signals into a form that can be transmitted over the system. Finally, there is a cost of amplifiers or repeaters along the cable. Because of the terminal cost, short-haul multiplex systems *prove in* only when the distance is great enough so that the terminals cost less than extra pairs of wires. This prove-in distance is five to twenty miles.

Two forms of short-haul systems are in common use. A simple frequency-division system (a system called type N is typical) transmits twelve double sideband or twenty-four single sideband channels by means of frequency-division multiplex. The standard repeater spacing for N carrier systems is five miles. A more recent development is the use of time-division pulse code modulation systems. Typically (in a system called T1), twenty-four telephone channels are transmitted, using a pulse rate of a little over 1.5 million pulses per second. Transistorized repeaters of high reliability, which can be mounted in manholes, are used every mile. Other possible transmission systems include microwave radio for short-haul traffic.

The T1 pulse code modulation system is used for distances from 5 to 50 miles; while a simple frequency-division system such as N is used for distances as long as 200 miles. For longer distances it is more economical to transmit hundreds of channels over a coaxial cable or a microwave radio link (or a submarine cable, or a communication satellite). *Long-haul* systems must have terminals that are efficient in squeezing many channels into the frequency band used, and the repeaters must be so finely designed that they will not add excessive noise or crosstalk in a total transmission path 4000 miles long.

At present, all long-haul systems use frequency-division multiplex, though a system is being designed which will transmit 4032 telephone signals in one direction through one coaxial by means of pulse code modulations. The pulse rate will be 281 million pulses per second, and the repeater spacing will be 1.25 miles. *Coaxial cables* consist of twenty coaxials, often called *pipes,* together with a number of twisted pairs, bound together in a single outer sheath. Ten coaxials are used for transmission in each direction, so the new system will provide 36,288 telephone channels in each direction. (One coaxial is reserved as a spare for each direction to provide for maintenance and reliability.)

All long-haul frequency-division systems make use of a standard pattern in shifting the frequencies of voice channels and combining them. This is illustrated in Fig. 30. A *channel bank* combines twelve voice channels into a *group* by shifting their frequencies. A *group bank* combines five groups into a *supergroup* (sixty channels) by another frequency shift. A *supergroup* bank combines ten supergroups into a *mastergroup* (600 channels) by means of still another frequency shift. By a further frequency shift, several mastergroups can be sent over one long-haul system.

Because of this hierarchical procedure, various channels of bandwidth broader than a telephone channel are easily available in the telephone network. These are the group, with a bandwidth of about 48,000 cycles; the supergroup, with a band-

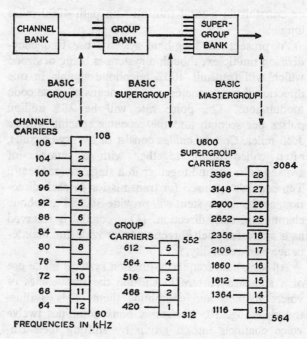

Figure 30

width of about 240,000 cycles; and the mastergroup, with a bandwidth of about 2,500,000 cycles. Such broadband channels can be valuable in data transmission and in facsimile transmission. In addition, broadband systems are used for television channels which have a bandwidth somewhat greater than four megacycles. In long-distance television transmission the sound signal is transmitted over a different circuit than that used to transmit the picture.

The most advanced coaxial cable system now in

use is the L4 system, which can transmit 3600 voice channels over each coaxial or pipe (72,000 over the twenty pipes in a cable) over a distance as great as 4000 miles. Frequencies lying between $\frac{1}{2}$ megacycle and $18\frac{1}{2}$ megacycles are used for messages, pilot (regulating) signals, and command signals. The repeater spacing is two miles.

Much long-haul traffic is handled by microwave radio systems. The repeaters in such systems must be in sight of one another, for microwaves travel in beams like the light of a searchlight. Thus, the receiving and transmitting antennas of a microwave repeater are mounted on towers, preferably on hilltops, at an average spacing of from 20 to 30 miles.

The long-haul microwave systems used in the Bell System are the TD-2 and TD-3, which operate in a frequency range from 3700 to 4200 megacycles, and the TH, which operates in a frequency range from 5925 to 6425 megacycles. The TH system provides six working and two protection channels, each handling up to 1860 telephone channels. TD-2 provides ten working channels and two protection channels, each handling up to 900 telephone channels. The TD-3 is the newest long-haul system. Like TD-2, it provides ten working and two protection channels. However, each channel handles 1200 telephone circuits.

In Chapter I we discussed some of the requirements which must be met in transmitting telephone signals. We saw how these requirements and the statistics of telephone conversations and telephone use dictate the ratio of the signal power at which the amplifiers of a frequency-division multiplex system overload to the noise power. This is one aspect of the challenging and complicated problem of matching signals to channels, which we discussed further in Chapters III and IV.

Why were transmissions systems built as they were? What are their limitations and potentialities? As the art and use of communication advance, should new transmission systems be different from those which are now in use?

Early multiplex systems were designed primarily to provide telephone channels over cables. The transmission loss or attenuation (expressed in db per mile) of a pair of wires or of a coaxial increases as the square root of the frequency. Thus, it seems reasonable to combine channels by shifting them in frequency, so that the highest frequency to be transmitted is only a little greater than the bandwidth of a single channel times the number of channels.

Because transmission loss increases with frequency, the power used per channel in transmitting the various channels is higher for the channels transmitted at higher frequencies.

Information theory tells us that to achieve the greatest channel capacity for a given total power and repeater spacing, power should be transmitted over a very much broader band, with the transmitted power almost the same at all frequencies. This is a theoretical result. We don't know how to build such a system.

A very high-speed pulse code modulation system such as the one referred to earlier does use a much broader bandwidth than a frequency-division system such as L4. Moreover, in such a system regenerative repeaters are used, so that the noise does not accumulate as the system length is increased. Does this make such a system more efficient than a frequency-division system? Much of the transmitted power is concentrated at high frequencies in order to overcome the high transmission loss at those frequencies. For the same repeater spacing and power, such a system will carry fewer telephone channels than a frequency-division system. Why, then, should one build such a system?

A common carrier communication system is used to transmit many sorts of signals besides telephone signals. Particularly, binary *data* signals for computers and business machines are increasing in volume. One can easily transmit around 2000 binary digits per second over any telephone channel, and by means of elaborate terminal equipment (using multilevel pulses and special automatically adjusted equalizers) one can transmit nearly 10,000 bits per second. But a pulse code modulation system uses 64,000 bits per second in transmitting one telephone channel. Hence, if we do want to transmit data, a pulse code modulation system transmits many more bits per second in place of one telephone channel than a frequency-division system does.

Here we have a conflict of economics. In long-haul transmission over coaxial cable, for telephony a pulse code modulation system using binary, off-on pulses costs a little more per telephone channel than a comparable frequency-division system, while for digital transmission a frequency-division system costs a lot more per bit per second than a pulse code modulation system. Which one will build depends on what is to be transmitted. But the problem is much more complicated. If we would successfully transmit eight or sixteen pulse amplitudes instead of two, a pulse code modulation system could transmit more telephone channels than a comparable frequency-division system.

Beyond this, how does microwave radio compare with coaxial cable? The first cost is lower for microwave systems but the operating cost is higher. Cable can be hardened against atomic explosions; microwave radio cannot. Reliability is somewhat different. Only a limited number of microwave systems can be operated in one area without interference among them; any amount of cable can be laid on one area.

And, beyond cable and microwave lies the possibility of transmitting 200 television signals or 100,-000 two-way telephone conversations through one two-inch pipe or waveguide by means of "millimeter" radio waves with frequencies of from 30,000 to 100,000 megacycles. A single communication satellite could provide over 100,000 telephone channels. Further in the future lies the possibility of communication by means of light generated by lasers and guided through long, buried tubes by means of lenses of heated gas.

What will communication of the future be like? We cannot really know until that future arrives. But we can be sure that it will involve new and powerful technologies, and that it will serve man better than the communication of the past or of the present.

Initially, in primitive electrical communication we had at our disposal two apparently distinct inventions. One of these was the telegraph, which communicated by on-off signals that produced audible clicks. The receiving operator interpreted these clicks as letters and words of a message and he transcribed the message to a piece of paper, or, in some instances, he spoke it to an expectant and waiting officer.

The other early invention was the telephone of Alexander Graham Bell, which transmitted, over a limited distance and faintly, the sound of the human voice. This device could be used either for conversation, or to transmit an order to a store, where a clerk faithfully wrote the order down.

This distinction has gradually disappeared as telegraph signals were multiplexed, or transmitted many at a time, over telephone lines, in much the way that Alexander Graham Bell had envisioned in his work on the harmonic telegraph, and as it became clear that telephone signals could be transmitted by off-on impulses, by pulse code modulation. And new forms of communication, facsimile, and television, and Picturephone, and data from computers, are all transmitted over the same facilities. Shannon's communication theory has helped us to appreciate the comprehensive nature of communication channels. His universal measure and universal unit of information—the *bit* (or binary digit)—applies equally well to the information rates and channel capacities of speech signals, and picture signals, and telegraph signals, and the signals that run around in modern electronic digital computers. It is only the limitations in our techniques of encoding that make some systems a bit more favorable to one sort of use, and others to another.

Everything in science and technology, including the sciences of the human body and of human behavior, and the technology of electrical communication and of our insight into it, tells us that communication and communication means are one flexible resource which can be adapted to human use in many ways. All our experience with the world teaches us that we want as much and as varied communication as possible. Everything we know about human beings and everything we know about electrical communication backs this up.

We all found it was a great advance to go from silent pictures to the talkies, and no one would like to go back. It would seem a shame to deprive the lecturer of his ability to illustrate his points quantitatively or graphically at the blackboard. Anyone who has seen a briefing at the Pentagon knows that the military would be helpless without colored slides as well as words. We all see and use a mixture of reading and writing, listening and speaking, and even gesturing in everyday discourse.

Electrical communication is an adaptation of science and technology to the service of man. Whatever new techniques communication of the future may bring, the over-all course of electrical communications must be that of using electromagnetic waves more flexibly in providing men with all the sorts of communication they want or need, either in communicating with other human beings, or with or through the computers which are their servants.

Decibels

The *decibel* is a measure of the ratio of two powers. The abbreviation for decibels is *db*. If we have two powers, P_2 and P_1, the power P_2 is said to be

$$10 \log_{10} (P_2/P_1)$$

decibels greater than P_1. For example, consider the following cases:

$$P_2 = 1,000,000, \qquad P_1 = 1000$$
$$P_2/P_1 = 1000$$
$$10 \log_{10} (P_2/P_1) = 30 \text{ db}$$
$$P_2 = 1000, \qquad P_1 = 1$$
$$10 \log_{10} (P_2/P_1) = 30 \text{ db}$$

The number of decibels depends only on the ratio. For various ratios we see that

P_2/P_1	db
1000	30
100	20
20	13
1	0
1/10	−1
1/200	−23

Decibels are sometimes used to measure power with respect to some standard value, such as a milliwatt

(10^{-3} watt). Thus a power of 10 dbm (db with respect to a milliwatt) means that

$$10 \log_{10} \left(\frac{\text{Power in watts}}{.001 \text{ watt}} \right) \text{ dbm}$$

Another reference of power is *reference noise*. Power in *dbrn* (db with respect to reference noise) is

$$10 \log_{10} \left(\frac{\text{Power in watts}}{10^{-12} \text{ watt}} \right) \text{ dbrn}$$

Why are decibels used? Suppose we have an amplifier with a power gain of 10 followed by an amplifier with a power gain of 1000. The total gain is

$$10 \times 1000 = 10,000$$

The gain of the first amplifier can be specified in decibels as

$$10 \log_{10} 10 = 10 \text{ db}$$

The gain of the second amplifier can be specified as

$$10 \log_{10} 1000 = 30 \text{ db}$$

The sum of these gains, 40 db, is just the gain of the two amplifiers in tandem

$$10 \log_{10} 10,000 = 40 \text{ db}$$

If we express gains in db, we can find the over-all gain simply by adding the db. For instance, suppose that a radio transmitter transmits a power of 10,000 mw (10 watts), or

$$40 \text{ dbm}$$

Suppose that a receiving antenna picks up only

Appendix I

1/1,000,000 of this, so that the loss in transmission is

$$10 \log_{10}(1/1,000,000) = -60 \text{ db}$$

Then the received power will be

$$40 + (-60) = -20 \text{ dbm},$$

or 1/100 of a milliwatt.

Waves and Frequencies

Some readers who don't have *Electrons and Waves* at hand may be puzzled by references to waves and frequencies.

Imagine a long, smooth wave in the ocean to go past a buoy, which will rise and fall as the wave passes. We can measure the time T between the passing of two crests; this is called the *period* of the wave. The number of crests per second, which we will call f, is the *frequency* of the wave. Clearly,

$$f = \frac{1}{T}$$

Looking at the waves, we may estimate the distance between crests; this is the wavelength, which is always denoted by the Greek letter λ (lambda).

The time between the passage of crests is T. In this time the next crest must travel just one wavelength, λ, to reach the position of the preceding crest. Thus, the wave travels with a velocity v which is this distance of travel, λ, divided by the elapsed time, T, so that

$$v = \frac{\lambda}{T} = \lambda f$$

Light waves and radio waves are both electromagnetic waves, and in air or in interplanetary space the velocity of light waves and radio waves is

126

$$v = 186,000 \text{ miles/second}$$
$$= 3 \times 10^8 \text{ meters/second}$$

Waves may of course have various shapes. But usually, when scientists and engineers talk about waves they mean *sinusoidal* waves. Sinusoidal waves rise and fall smoothly with distance (or with time) as they pass by us. Fig. 31 shows a sinusoidal wave.

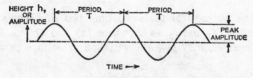

Figure 31

Many electrical signals vary in a quite complicated way with time or distance. But we can represent such a complicated variation as a sum of sinusoidal variations of waves having different frequencies. Thus, when we say that a telephone signal covers a band of frequencies from 200–3200 cycles (strictly, cycles per second), we mean that the signal can be represented accurately by many sine waves whose frequencies lie in the range 200–3200 cycles, and that no sine waves with frequencies outside of this range are needed to give an accurate representation.

Frequency Shifting

Suppose we have at the same time two sine waves of frequencies f_1 and f_2, as shown in (a) and (b) of Fig. 32. Together, they give the variation of voltage or cur-

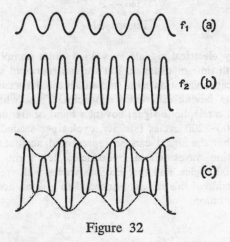

Figure 32

rent with time which is shown by the solid line in (c) of the figure.

The dotted line in (c) of Fig. 32 is called the *envelope* of the combined wave. It has a frequency $f_2 - f_1$. The envelope does not represent the voltage, or the current, or anything physically present. But, by

Appendix III

using a *rectifier* or *diode* and a *band pass filter* we can produce a voltage or current equal to the envelope.

Suppose we want to shift the frequency of a wave of frequency f_1. We add a wave of frequency f_2, and use a rectifier and a filter to obtain a wave of frequency $f_2 - f_1$. The combination of a rectifier and a filter which we use to shift the frequency is called a *modulator*.

Besides producing a signal of frequency $f_2 - f_1$, a modulator can be used to produce a signal of frequency $f_2 + f_1$ (it is not so easy to see that this is so). This is valuable when we want to shift the frequencies of a signal wave to a higher band of frequencies.

For instance, suppose we want to shift the frequencies of a voice signal, frequencies from 200 to 3200 cycles, to a range from 30,200 to 33,200 cycles. We can use a modulator and a wave from a *local oscillator* with a frequency, called a *carrier frequency,* of 30,000 cycles.

If we want to shift the frequencies back to the range 200–3200 cycles, we can use the $f_2 - f_1$ output of a modulator, again using a local oscillator or carrier frequency of 30,000 cycles.

When we shift the frequencies of a signal by means of a carrier frequency, the shifted frequencies are called *sidebands* of the carrier frequency. Thus, if we shift voice frequencies lying between 200 and 3200 cycles to the range 30,200 to 33,200 cycles by means of a 30,000-cycle carrier frequency, the shifted frequencies lying between 30,200 and 33,200 cycles are called sideband frequencies or, collectively, a sideband.

In AM (amplitude modulation) radio there are two sidebands, one below and one above the carrier frequency (the assigned frequency of the broadcasting station). This situation exists in FM also, but in FM each sideband covers a greater range of frequencies than the original signal does.

Index

ABC, 97

Acoustics, 7 ff.

See also Hearing; Speech

Active channels, 16

Adaptive networks, 96–97

Aluminum foil, 113

AM (amplitude modulation), 44, 52 ff., 55, 129

American Telephone & Telegraph Company, 93, 97

Amount of information, defined, 67

Amplifiers, 14, 20, 29, 44

telephonic, 6, 113, 114, 117

unattended, reliability of, 88

Amplitude modulation. *See* AM

Amplitudes, 44, 46–64, 78, 120

See also AM; FM; Frequencies; Modulation; PCM

Andover, Maine, 94

Antennas, 41

microwave, 90 ff., 99 ff., 117

Apollo program, 97, 98–104

Architecture, 98

Arizona, 88

Armstrong, Edwin H., 53–54

Army, U.S., communications satellites and, 88, 93, 103

Articulation, 13

defined, 10–11

Astrogation, 88

AT&T, 93, 97

Atmosphere, space communications and, 86, 87, 89, 92

Atomic explosions, 120

Attenuation, 118

See also Loss of power

Audio signals, 52–64

Automatic switching machinery, telephonic, 112, 113

Automobiles, 107–8

Average rates of information, 81–82, 83, 101–3

Average signal power, 15, 71

Balloon satellites, 89–93

Band pass filters, 129

Bandwidths, 43–64, 66, 71–82, 115 ff., 129 (*See also* Frequencies)

amount of information transmissible over, 71–82

Bandwidths (*cont'd*)
communication theory and, 71–82
reduction of, 60–64, 75 ff.
space photography and, 99–100
Batteries, satellite, 88–89, 95
Bell, Alexander Graham, 6, 18, 107, 121
Bell System, 109, 111, 117
Bell Telephone Laboratories, 7, 90, 103
echo suppression study, 96
Bending, radio wave, 86
Berlin, 3
Binary digits, 69 ff., 78–85, 119
See also Bits of information
Binary signals, 62, 70 ff., 76–85, 119
Binary system, 70–85, 119
See also Binary digits; Binary signals
Bits of information, 69–71, 76, 83, 119
defined, 69
space photography and, 101–3
transmission of, 69–85, 101–3, 119
Boosters, 88, 93, 95, 97
Brightness. *See* Light and dark
British, the, 93
Broadband channels, 116
Broadband frequency modulation, 53–54, 66
Business machines, 119
Buzzing sounds, speech transmission of, 79–80

Cable:
coaxial, 41, 51, 75–76, 106, 114–20
pairs, 75–76
repeaters, 89, 104
submarine, 88, 89, 96, 104, 114
telephone, 88, 89, 96, 97, 104, 106, 113, 114–20
Camera lens, TV, 27, 28, 29
Candles. *See* Foot-candles
Canopus, 99
Capacitators, 41
Capacity. *See* Channel capacity
Carrier frequency, 129
Channel banks, 115, 116
Channel capacity, 71–75 ff., 77–85, 118
measuring, 77–78, 81
space photography and, 102, 103
Channels, communications, 41–64, 66, 71–85, 121
in space, 101–4
telephone, 15–18, 93, 94–97, 114, 115–21
Check digits, 83–85
Choices, 67–71, 82
Circuits:
interconnecting, 95–97, 109–21
program, 2
Clarke, Arthur C., 87
Cloudy days, telecasting on, 26, 32–33
Coaxial cables, 41, 51, 75–76, 106, 114–20
described, 115
economics of, 119–20
Codes, coding (*See also* Decoders; Encoders)
error-correcting, 83–85
information theory and, 69, 74, 76 ff., 103

Codes, coding (*cont'd*)
  telegraphy (Morse), 5–6, 56
  transmission and, 56, 57–64, 74, 76 ff., 103
  See also specific systems
Coherent light, 106
  See also Lasers
Command signals, 117
Commercial communication systems (*See also* Common carrier communication systems; specific systems)
  space satellites and, 93, 95, 97
Common carrier communication systems, 1, 97, 104, 119–21
  See also Commercial communication systems
Communications channels. *See* Channels, communications
Communications satellites, 38–39, 87–104, 120
Communication (information) theory, 65–85, 118, 121
  space photography and, 101–4
Communications Satellite Act, 97
Communications Satellite Corporation. *See* COMSAT
Communications systems, 1 ff., 105–21 (*See also* Channels, communications; Communication theory; Telegraphy; Telephones; Television; Transmission systems; specific devices, prob-

lems, techniques)
  design of, 14–18
  space and, 86–104
  typical, diagram, 76
Computers, electronic, 41, 90, 106, 119, 121
  binary system and, 70–71
  communication theory and, 83
COMSAT, 97
Cost (economics):
  communications satellites and, 93, 97, 103–4
  telephonic interconnections and, 113–14, 119–20
Courier 1-B, 93
Crawford Hill, N.J., 90, 91
Current, 5, 6, 19, 25 ff., 31 ff. (*See also* Frequencies; Power; Voltage)
  defined, 31
  frequency shifting, 128–29
  telegraphy, 4–5
Cybernetics (Wiener), 67
Cycles, 8–11 ff., 78, 115 ff., 127, 129
  See also Frequencies

Darkness. *See* Light and dark
Data, 83, 92, 116, 119, 121 (*See also* Bits of information)
  defined, 76
Db. *See* Decibels
Dbrn, 124
Dbrnc, 13–14, 124
Decibels (db), 7–17, 39, 123–25
  defined, 7–8, 123
  space communication and, 91, 99

Decibels (db) (*cont'd*)
transmission loss expressed in, 118, 124–25
Decimal system, 70
Decisions. *See* Choices
Decoders, decoding, 74, 76–77
See also Coders
Density, atmospheric, 87, 89
Destination, signal, 77, 78
Dialing network, map, 111, 112
Diaphragms, telephone, 6
Digits. *See also* Bits of information
binary, 69 ff., 78 ff.
check and message, 83–85
Diodes, 128
Direct distance dialing, 112
Dishes, microwave antennas as, 90
Disk. *See* Nipkow disk
Distance dialing network, map of, 111, 112
Distortion, nonlinear, 14, 15
Dudley, Homer, 79

Ear (*See also* Hearing; Speech)
sensitivity to sound in, 7–18
Early Bird, 97
Earth stations (earth terminals; ground stations), 87, 90, 91, 92, 93, 94, 97, 99
coding schemes using error correction and, 103
Echo I, 89–93, 94, 95
Echo suppressors, 96
Economics. *See* Cost
Eisenhower, Dwight D., 88, 90
Electrical communication,

significance and future of, 105 ff., 120–21
Electric telegraphy, 4–6, 120–21
Electrodes, TV and, 21, 30 ff.
Electromagnetic waves, 41–64, 75, 86 ff., 105, 107–21, 122, 126–27
velocity of, 126–27
Electromagnets, 4, 5, 6
Electron beams, TV and, 20–39, 81
Electronic computers. *See* Computers
Electronic equipment, communication through space and, 89 ff.
Electronic switching, 106
Electron multipliers, 28, 29–33, 35
illustrated, 28, 30
Electrons and Waves, 8 n, 106
Electron tubes, 6, 41
See also Tubes; specific kinds
Elementary choices, 69
See also Bits of information
Encoders, encoding, 74, 76, 82–85, 121
space photography and, 101–3
Entropy, 81–82, 83, 101–3
Envelope, 128–29
Errors:
channel capacity and, 72, 83, 103
correction of, 83–85
correction in space, 103
Eyes. *See* Vision

Facsimile transmission, 92, 116, 121

Farnsworth, Philo T., 28
FCC. *See* Federal Communications Commission
Federal Communications Commission, 53, 97
Filters:
  band pass, 129
  frequency selection and, 42, 44, 51
  speech frequencies and, 79–80
Fletcher, Harvey, 7, 9
FM (frequency modulation), 52–54, 59, 63, 129
  band of frequencies covered by, 66, 129
  information transmission and, 73–81
Foot-candles, 26–27, 28, 31, 32, 36, 37
Force, meaning in physics, 67
Ford Foundation, 97
Four-wire transmission, 113
France, 93, 105
  Paris, 3
Freedom. *See* Choices
Frequencies, 8–18, 39–40, 42–44 ff., 66, 126–27 (*See also* Bandwidths; Hearing; Noise; Telephones; Television)
  carrier, 129
  communication through space and, 86, 87
  defined, explained, 8, 126–27
  shifting of, 14, 42, 48 ff., 92, 115, 128–29
  telephonic interconnections and, 113–21
  waves and, 126–29

Frequency-division multiplex, 14, 16, 42, 43, 44–48 ff., 62, 63
  space communication and, 92
  telephone interconnections and, 113 ff., 117–19
Frequency modulation. *See* FM
Frequency repeaters. *See* Repeaters, frequency

Gas-heated lenses, 120
Gemini space program, 98
Georgia, 88
Golay, Marcel J. E., 83
Goldstone, Calif., 90, 91
Great Britain, 93
Ground stations. *See* Earth stations
Group banks, 115, 116
Guard bands, 51

Hamming, R. W., 83
Harmonic telegraph, 121
Hearing (*See also* Frequencies; Noise; Sound intensity; Sound waves; Speech)
  information theory and, 78
  nature of, 7 ff.
  telephone systems and, 6–18, 41
  See also Telephones
Hissing sounds, speech transmission and, 79–80
Hughes Aircraft Company, 95
Hybrid coils, 96

Iconoscope, 33

Illumination. *See* Foot-candles; Light and dark; Light waves; Lumens

Image dissector tube, 28–33, 35–36, 37

Image intensifier orthicon, 38

Image orthicon, 33–38

Index of modulation, 52–53, 63, 66, 73–75

Inductors, 41

Information (*See also* Bits of information)
 defined, 67

Information rate, 77–82, 83, 101–3

Information (communication) theory, 65–85, 118, 121
 space photography and, 101–4

Intensity levels. *See* Decibels; Frequencies; Hearing; Loudness; Sound intensity

Interchannel interference, 15

Interconnections, telephonic, 109–21

Interference, 15

Interlaced scanning, 22–23, 25, 39

Interoffice trunks, 109, 110, 113

Ionosphere, 86, 87

Jet Propulsion Laboratory, 89, 90

Johnson noise, 27–28, 31, 37
 communications systems and, 71
 defined, 25–26
 space communication and, 92, 100

Keys, telegraph, 5, 6

Kompfner, Rudolf, 89

Langley Research Laboratory, 89

Language, meaning and, 67

Lasers, 106, 120

Lengths of waves, 126

Lenses, 86
 gas-heated, 120
 TV camera, 27, 28, 29

L4 coaxial cable system, 117, 118

Light and dark, TV transmission and, 19–39, 41, 43, 44, 81
 in space, 101–2

Light waves, 41, 86, 120, 126–27
 communication by means of, 120
 lasers, 106, 120
 propagation, 86
 television and, 41 (*see also* Television)
 velocity, 126–27

Lincoln Laboratory (MIT), 103

Local central offices, 109, 110

Local oscillators, 129

Logarithms, 72, 75

Long-distance (trunk) telephone circuits, 15–17, 95–97, 109–21

Long-haul systems, 114–15, 119–21

Loss of power, 113, 118, 119, 124–25

Loudness, 2, 96
 telephone subscribers' preferences in, 11

Loudspeakers, 77

Lumens, 26, 27, 31, 36, 37

Mariner space vehicles, 38, 98–104
    Mariner IV, 98–104
Marketing, 108
Mars, 98–104
Masking of speech, noise and, 11
Massachusetts Institute of Technology. *See* MIT
Mastergroups, 115, 116
"Mathematical Theory of Communication, A," 67, 83, 102, 103, 121
Mathematics, information theory and, 67, 68–71, 72, 78–79
Maxwell, James Clerk, 86
Men's voices, ears and, 9
Mercury program, 98
Messages (*See also* Communications systems; Signals; Speech; Transmission systems; specific aspects, problems, systems)
    choice in transmission of, 68–71, 82
    error-free, 83–85, 103
Microphones, 76, 77, 80
Microwave antennas, 90 ff., 99 ff., 117
Microwave channels, 51, 73, 75, 106
    telephone interconnections and, 114, 117–21
Microwave radio, 75, 106, 114, 117–21
Microwave repeaters, 117
Microwave telephony, 114, 117–21
Military equipment, time-division frequency used in, 51

Millimeter radio waves, 106, 120
MIT, 103
Modulation, 44, 52 ff., 58–64 (*See also* AM; Amplitudes; FM; Frequencies; PCM)
    index of, 52–53, 63, 66, 73–75
    noise and, 53 ff., 73 ff., 103 (*see also* Noise)
    space communication and, 92
Modulators, frequency shifting by means of, 14, 92, 129
Moon program, 97, 98–104
Morse, Samuel F. B., 4–5
Morse code, 5–6
Multichannel multiplex system, 14–15
Multiple-amplitude pulses, 62
Multiplex systems, 14–15, 113–21
    See also Frequency-division multiplex; Time-division multiplex
Multipliers, electron, 28, 29–33, 35
    illustrated, 28, 30

NASA, 89, 93, 95, 104
National Advisory Committee for Aeronautics, 89
National Aeronautics and Space Administration. *See* NASA
N carrier systems, 114
New York City, 112
Nipkow, Paul Gottlieb, 20
Nipkow disk, 24–29, 37
    illustrated, 24

Noise, 2, 11–18, 25–27, 31, 32, 36–40, 50 ff. (*See also* Hearing; Power; Signals; Speech)
  communications systems and, 71–84, 92, 93–103 (*see also* specific systems)
  electromagnetic wave transmission and, 42, 50–64
  Johnson (*see* Johnson noise)
  modulation and, 53 ff., 73 ff., 103
  quantizing, 59, 63–64, 103
  reference, 124
  shot, 38
  space communication and, 92, 99–103
  -to-signal ratio, 2, 14, 59 ff., 73 ff., 81, 92, 117–19
Nonlinear distortion, 14, 15
North America, telephone interconnections, 109–21

Offices, interconnecting, 109–12
Open wire, 112–13
Oscillator, local, 129
O'Sullivan, William J., 89
Overload, 14, 15, 118

Parabolic antennas, 90
Paris, 3
PCM (pulse-code modulation), 58–60, 63–64, 73–78, 81
  noise and, 58–59, 63, 73 ff.
  telephone interconnections and, 114 ff., 118–21
Period, wave, 126

Petrograd, 3
Photocathodes, 27 ff., 31, 33, 34, 35, 36, 37, 38
Photoelectric cells, TV and, 25, 26
Photography (*See also* Television)
  space, 38–39, 98–104
Pickering, William H., 89
Pickup devices and systems, TV, 19–40
  See also Picture elements; specific devices, systems
Picture elements, transmission of, 20–21, 23–40, 43 ff., 57, 121
  information theory and, 71, 81, 121
  space communication and, 99–104
Picturephone, 121
Pilot (regulating) signals, 117
Pipes, signal transmission through, 106, 115, 117, 120
  See also Coaxial cables
Pitch, 79, 80
  See also Frequencies; Hearing; Modulation; Speech
Plastic foil, 113
Portrules, 4, 5
Power, 13–18, 20 ff. (*See also* Noise; Signals; Transmission systems; specific devices)
  average, 15, 71
  decibels and, 7–8, 13–14, 123–24
  loss, 113, 118, 119, 124–25
  signal-to-noise ratio and, 14, 59 ff., 73 ff., 81, 92, 99–100, 102, 117–19

Power (*cont'd*)
space communication and, 90 ff., 99–102
Primary offices, 112
Program circuits, 2
Propagation, wave, 86
Prove-in distances, 114
Prussia, 3
Psychoacoustics, 7
Pulse-code modulation. *See* PCM
Pulse positions, 55–60 ff.
Pulses, 46 ff., 55–64 (*See also* PCM)
as samples of the signal, 46
telephonic interconnections and, 114, 118–21

Quanta, TV and, 37
Quantizing noise, 59, 63–64, 103
Quantum electronics, 92
Quantum Electronics, 106
Quantum theory, 37

Radiation, space communication and, 94–95
Radio, 1, 2, 86 ff.
See also Communications systems; Radio receivers; specific parts, systems, techniques
Radio receivers, 77 ff., 88, 90, 91 ff.
Radio transmitters, 76 ff., 88, 89, 90 ff.
Radio waves, 41, 52–54, 75 ff., 126–27, 129
communication through space and, 86–104
short (millimeter), 106, 120

telephone interconnections and, 114, 117–21
velocity, 126–27
Ranger satellite, 38
Rate of information, 77–82, 83, 101–3
Rate of transmission, 77–78, 81–82
See also Channel capacity
Ratio, decibel, 7–8, 13–14, 123–25
Ratio of received power to transmitted power, 90–91, 99–100
Ratio of signal-to-noise power, 2, 14, 59 ff., 73 ff., 81, 92, 117–19
space communication and, 90–91, 92, 100, 101
RCA, 95
Rectifiers, 129
Reduction of bandwidths, 60–64, 75–76
Reference noise, 13, 124
Reflectors, parabolic, 90
Regenerators, 55–59, 118–19
Regional offices, 112
Relay I satellite, 95
Reliability, as characteristic of communications systems, 87, 95, 104, 115, 119
Repeaters, frequency, 113, 114, 115
regenerative, 118–19
spacing of, 115, 117
submarine telephone cable, 88, 89, 104
Resistors, 25, 27, 41
Retrace, TV, 22

St. Paul, Minn., 107, 108

Sampling, samples, 49–51, 57–60, 62–64
 defined, 46
Satellites, communications, 87–104, 120
 photographs from, 38–39, 98–104
Scanning, TV, 22–28, 29, 32, 35, 38, 39, 81
Science, electrical communication and, 107, 122
Score satellite, 88–89
Secondary electrons, 30, 34
Sectional offices, 112
Semaphore telegraphs, 3–4
Shade. *See* Light and dark
Shannon, Claude:
 law of maximum bits transmittable, 71–74, 77, 102, 103
 "A Mathematical Theory of Communication," 67, 83, 102, 103, 121
Shapes of waves, 127
Shifting, frequency, 42, 48 ff., 92, 115, 128–29
Short-haul multiplex systems, 113–14
Shot noise, 38
Sidebands, 44, 92, 129
Signal destination, 77, 78
Signals (*See also* Communications systems; Frequencies; Messages; Modulation; Noise; Power; Signal-to-noise ratio; Speech; specific devices, techniques)
 channels and, 15–18, 42–64, 93–97, 114–21
 distortion in, 14, 15 (*see also* Noise)
 information theory and, 65 ff., 71 ff., 101–3

sampling, 46 ff.
 shifting of frequency in, 14, 42, 48 ff., 92, 115, 128–29
 space communication and, 86–104
 telegraphy, 3–6, 120–21
 telephony, 14–18, 95–97, 112–21, 127 (*see also* Telephones)
 television, 20–40, 120 (*see also* Television)
Signal source, 76 ff.
Signal-to-noise ratio, 2, 14, 59 ff., 73 ff., 81, 102, 117–19
 space communication and, 92, 99–100, 102
Sine (sinusoidal) waves, 14, 78–79, 127, 128–29
Single sideband, 92
Sinusoidal (sine) waves, 14, 78–79, 127, 128–29
"Snow," television, 2, 32, 39
Sounders, telegraph, 5, 6
Sound intensity, 10–17
 See also Decibels; Frequencies; Hearing; Loudness; Sound waves
Sound waves, 6 ff., 19, 41, 78–80
 See also Hearing; Sound intensity; Speech
Source, signal, 76 ff.
Space, communication in, 86–104
Space programs, U.S., 88–95, 97, 98–104
Space vehicles, 38, 88, 95
 See also Space, communication in, specific vehicles
Speech:
 amplitude and, 56 ff.

Speech (*cont'd*)
  frequencies in, 9 ff., 41–43, 51, 66, 77–82, 113–21
  hearing and, 6–18, 78 ff. (*see also* Hearing)
  pitch in, 79, 80
  power in, 15–18, 41–43, 113 ff. (*see also* Power)
  space communication and, 88, 89, 90, 92, 95
  telephonic interconnections and, 113–21 (*see also* Telephones)
  transmission of, 41–43, 56 ff., 76–82, 113–21 (*see also* Transmission systems)
  vocoders and, 79–82
Sputnik I, 87, 88
Storage principle, TV and, 33, 38–39
Stress, meaning as used in engineering, 67
Submarine cable, 88, 89, 96, 104, 114
Subscriber loops, 109, 110, 112–13
Sun, Mariner IV and, 99
Supergroup banks, 115, 116
Switching, electronic, 106
Synchronization, 23, 50
Synchronous satellites, 95–97
Syncom satellites, 95, 97

Tandem offices, 110
Tandem trunks, 110
Target screen, 34
TD-2 microwave system, 117
TD-3 microwave system, 117
Technology, electrical communication and, 107, 122
Telegraphy, 3–6, 120–21

Telephone poles, 112–13
Telephones and telephony, 2, 6–18, 41, 95, 105, 106, 107–21
  cable transmission, 88, 89, 96, 97, 104, 106, 113, 114, 118, 119–20
  channels, 93, 94–97, 101–4, 114, 115–21
  electromagnetic waves and, 41–43, 44, 51, 56 ff., 107–21
  information theory and, 66
  interconnections, 109–21
  space and, 93, 94–97, 101–4
Teletypewriters, 2
Television, 2, 18, 19–40, 120, 121 (*See also* specific parts, systems, techniques)
  communications satellites and, 93–95, 97, 101–4
  electromagnetic waves and, 41, 43 ff., 93–95
  information theory and, 66, 71, 73 ff., 76, 80–81, 82
  long-distance transmission, 93–97, 116
  Telstar and, 93–95
  transatlantic, 93–97
Television networks, communications satellites and, 97
Telstar satellite, 93–95
Temperature, 27–28
  communication through space and, 86, 92, 99–100
Texas, 88
TH microwave system, 117

Thor-Delta launching vehicle, 95

Time-division multiplex, 44 ff., 62–64
telephone interconnections and, 113, 114–15

Time sequences, TV and, 19–40, 42 ff.
See also Time-division multiplex

Toll circuits, 110–12, 113

Toll offices, 110, 113

T1 pulse-code modulation system, 114, 115

Touch-Tone dialing, 112

Toulon, 3

Tracking, 90, 92, 99

Transatlantic telephone and TV, 88, 89, 93–97

Transistors, 41, 113, 114

Transmission rate, 2, 77–78, 81–82
See also Channel capacity

Transmission systems, 1 ff., 41–64, 65 ff., 106–21 (*See also* Communications systems; Telephones; Television; specific devices, problems, systems)
communications satellites and, 88, 89, 90–104
error-free, 83–85 (*see also* Errors)
long-distance telephony, 95, 112–21
photography in space and, 98–104

Traveling-wave tubes, 94

Trier, 3

Trunks, interconnecting, 109 ff.

Tubes, electron:
as amplifiers in telephony, 6, 106 (*see also* Amplifiers, telephonic)
radio, 1
television pickup and picture, 21–40, 81, 106
See also Picture elements

Tubes, metal (*See also* Pipes)
waveguides, 41, 86, 106, 120

Tyros satellite, 38

Uncertainty, 67–71, 82

Underwater telephone cables, 88, 89, 96

United States (*See also* specific agencies, individuals, satellites)
space program, 88–95, 97, 98–104

United States Army, 88, 93, 103

United States Information Agency, 93

United States Public Health Service, 7

Universality, 108–9

Vacuum tubes, 29, 41

Vail, Alfred, 4–5

Velocity, wave, 126–27

Vidicons, 38

Vision, TV pickup and, 19 ff., 41 ff.
See also Television

Vocoders, 79–82

Voice, 6–18
See also Hearing; Speech; Telephones

Voice frequency repeaters, 113, 114, 115, 117

Voltage, 6, 29 ff., 42 ff., 53 (*See also* Current; Frequencies; Power; Watts)

Voltage (*cont'd*)
  frequency shifting, 129
    (*see also* Shifting)
  radio signal, 53
  telephone, 6, 42–43
  television, 29 ff., 44 ff.
Vu (volume units), 11, 14
Vu meters, 11

Watts, 8, 13
  See also Current; Cycles;
    Power; Voltage
Waveguides, 41, 86, 106, 120
Wavelength, defined, 126

Weighting factors, 12, 40
Western Union, 97
Wide deviation frequency
  modulation, 92
Wiener, Norbert, 67
Wire transmission circuits,
  75–76, 112–13, 118
  See also specific kinds,
    systems
Women's voices, 9
World War II, 66

Zworykin, Vladimir K., 33